MICHAEL COLLINS
THE IRISH REPUBLICAN BRO

VINCENT MacDOWELL

Vincent MacDowell is a native of Newry, County Down.

He is a retired engineer and publisher and comes from three generations of a strongly Republican family. His grandfather, Peter Fox, was County Organiser of the IRB in County Down, and Peter's son, Charles, was Head Centre of the IRB in Newry. His mother, Nora (*née* McDowell), was a member of Cumann na mBan and spent three years in Armagh prison.

At the age of 16 years, Vincent was interned for three years in Crumlin Road Prison, Belfast. He was later involved in organising the Irish Labour Party in Belfast, and came to live in Dun Laoghaire in 1952.

He retained his interest in Northern affairs, and was vice-chairman of the Northern Ireland Civil Rights Association in 1969 and 1970. He is an active member of the Green Party.

Michael Collins
and the Irish Republican Brotherhood

VINCENT MacDOWELL

ASHFIELD
Press

This book was typeset by
Gough Typesetting Services for
Ashfield Press,
an imprint of Blackhall Publishing Ltd,
26 Eustace Street. Dublin 2.
(e-mail: blackhall@tinet.ie)

A catalogue record for this book
is available from the British Library

ISBN 1-901658-05-8 pbk
ISBN 1-901658-06-6 hbk

Printed by
Betaprint Ltd.

Contents

Acknowledgements

The sources from which I have drawn this narrative are many and varied, include more than 40 books, and collections of papers, too many to list. I cannot pass, however, without acknowledging a debt to the following, amongst many:

Coogan, T.P., *Michael Collins;* Coogan, T.P., *De Valera, Long Fellow: Long Shadow;* Feehan, J.M., *The Shooting of Michael Collins;* O'Cuinnegáin, M., *On the Arm of Time;* MacEoin, U., *Survivors;* Beirne, J.O., *The IRB – Treaty to '24.*

I record with gratitude, conversations with Capt. J.M. Feehan, following convivial '68 Committee dinners, which aroused my detective instincts, and returned me to early family papers and records of Belfast in the late 40s, and many conversations with Paul Carleton, another childhood mentor of mine, and a former member of the Brotherhood and the Citizen Army. My mother had much information of meetings of the IRB at our family home, when she was a girl in Newry, before the Rising, mentioning in particular, Dr Pat McCartan, Head Centre of Tyrone, and Sean McDermott.

My maternal grandfather, Peter Fox of Newry, a noted bard and seanchaí, and a devotee of the memory of John Mitchel, gave me a rich store of memories. Peter, who lived in my home in Omeath at the end of his years, had been a Fenian from early days, and had watched Mitchel's burial in Newry, and had inaugurated a yearly commemoration of Mitchel, which I remember from my youth in the frontier town. He and Johnny Southwell had organised the Brotherhood in South Down and Armagh, and he, although taking the Republican side in the Civil War, had great respect and affection for Michael Collins.

His son, my uncle Charley Fox, was an active Brother, and a member of Aiken's staff in the 4th Northern Division, and Head Centre of the Brotherhood in Newry. He was present at the crucial meeting of Northern officers in Portobello, presided over by Collins, 2 August 1922, at which Collins outlined his future policies towards the Unionist Government and the Boundary Commission. Charley took the Republican side, and had to flee to the US, after the Civil War. There he joined the US Cavalry, and served with distinction until retirement in 1946, when he came back to Ireland to live out his years. He filled in many blanks in my understanding of how the immense tragedy of the Civil War unfolded. Another uncle, Mick O'Hare of Warrenpoint, was also a member of the Brotherhood, and fought in the 4th Northern.

Introduction

This book is not a simple historical novel, nor is it an official, documented chronicle of agreed facts. It is a hybrid – faction, tailored to fit the facts on the sound scientific principle that the simplest hypothesis that fits all the facts is usually the right one.

Robert Graves successfully explored a personal genre, which he shared with Mary Renault, and which he termed "the intuitive recollection of past events – the analeptic method".

Perhaps that is the nearest I can come to categorising this story, combining the eavesdropping on history, the sifting of personal recollections of survivors, and patient delving through little-used primary records.

The book is the story of a secret revolutionary society, the Irish Republican Brotherhood – IRB – which succeeded, after 65 years of effort, in wresting most of Ireland from the British Empire. This was the first of many liberation struggles in this century, and was to be a model for them all.

The book is also the story of the main leader in the revolution – Michael Collins, his busy life and his untimely death. The mystery of how and why ministers in his own Provisional Free State government were induced to collaborate with British intelligence, and facilitated his murder, is probed, and the killer named, (not as many Irishmen believe, Sonny O'Neill, or Emmet Dalton).

In order to explain the political imperatives that drove some members of Collin's Provisional Free State Government to facilitate his murder, and British Intelligence to execute it, I have transgressed some venerable Irish taboos, and doubtless will pay for it.

To understand and accept the events of 1922, culminating in the Civil War, I have had to breach some polite conventions. For instance, common knowledge – not mere gossip – numbers Moya Llewellyn Davies and Lady Hazel Lavery as Collin's lovers. I have had, to state it plainly, to explain the final blackmail of Collins on 5 December 1921, when he was forced to accept the Treaty against the instructions of the Brotherhood, well knowing the consequences. Both ladies concerned made no secret of their love affairs with Collins – quite the reverse. Less well-known is that he had two children by Moya, and fascinating echoes and coincidences rumble through the life of his son Richard, a Communist "Apostle" at Cambridge in the 30s, and a Labour peer in the 60s.

Collins was not a saint, and his youthful taurine concupiscence, and his sexual frolics with three London society ladies, are recorded, as far as they were relevant. But, the enduring love of his life was one of these, Moya Llewelyn Davies, née Moya O'Connor. She was married to the Solicitor-General of the British Government, Crompton Llewelyn-Davies and the story of the love between Moya and Michael is one of the great romances of the century. Michael and Moya had two children, a son named Richard, and a daughter, Kathleen, and the last happy moments of Collin's life were spent in Lady Moya's arms at Furry Park, Killester. She mourned his memory all the days of her life, and with it the cruel knowledge of how their love was used to blackmail and unbalance Collins in his supreme moment of crisis. Throughout the events described, the defining test is "Who profits?"

There are very rarely coincidences, very rarely simple fortunate (or unfortunate) accidents in matters of State. Most things are arranged and managed, with varying degrees of success, often by those organisations with centuries of experience at this sort of thing. James Jesus Angleton, CIA station chief in Europe during the Cold War, described intelligence work as working in a "Hall of Mirrors – nothing was ever what it seemed". As a professional glazier – mending broken mirrors – Spycatcher Peter Wright would agree. So also would Kevin O'Higgins, as he used the formula of Pearse "One man must die for the People", to explain the political necessity for the death of Collins.

A searchlight is shone on the operations of one of the branches of the British Secret Intelligence Service – MI6. The chicanery of the Welsh Warlock, David Lloyd-George, is central to the joint and common tragedy of British-Irish relationships, and is outlined.

From the beginning of the Irish revolution, a cruel destiny placed Collins in antagonism to his only rival for the affections of the Irish people – Eamonn De Valera. As Head Centre of the Irish Republican Brotherhood, Michael Collins was specified in their Constitution as President of the Irish Republic "now virtually established". When the first Irish Parliament, Dáil Éireann, met in January 1919, De Valera was elected as "Priomh Aire", Prime Minister of the Dáil, in which Collins was Minister for Finance, as well as holding important military posts, in acceptance of the IRB influence in the Dáil and the Irish Volunteers.

However, De Valera went on a tour of the United States almost as soon as he was freed from Lincoln Jail, and he succumbed to the unfortunate flattery of Joe McGarrity, the Brotherhood's second-in-command to John Devoy in the US, and permitted himself to be introduced as "President of the Irish Republic". Although this title had never been officially bestowed upon him , he retained it on returning to involve himself in the truce and treaty negotiations. Factions rapidly developed within the Cabinet, the Dáil, and the Army, between the supporters and friends of the "Invisible President", Collins, and the self-appointed usurper, De Valera.

This dichotomy led, with the inevitability of a classic Greek tragedy, towards De Valera's repudiation of the Treaty terms brought back to Ireland by

Collins - and the ensuing Civil War.

It is fruitless to say "If only?"

If only Collins had travelled in the armoured car, instead of the open Leyland tourer?

If only Collins had survived as President of the Executive Council, to oversee the work of the Boundary Commission, instead of the fatuous and incompetent Cosgrave?

If only DeValera had accepted his role as leader of the constitutional opposition, after the Dáil vote on the Treaty, in 1922, instead of five years and hundreds of deaths later in 1927?

If only Emmet Dalton had not fired on the Republican Army HQ in the Four Courts, with deliberate precipitate action, and waited until the peaceful surrender which was in progress, to be concluded four hours later?

To ask these questions is almost to answer them. It is not important to don a partisan approach to these cruel events. It is much more important that we understand them, and that we accept the actions of all the actors therein, of whatever side or nationality, with understanding and compassion, as resulting from their honest view at the time. The fact that they were often stupid and wrong – in hindsight – does not help. It may help to realise that, often first assumptions are wrong, and that anger and emotion are the worst possible guides to rational conduct. Cromwell – an odd person for an Irish Republican to quote – once said to the Parliament of the Commonwealth: "Gentlemen, I beseech you, by the bowels of Christ, Think that you may be wrong".

Vincent MacDowell

ONE

Blood Brothers

The tall broad shouldered youth, just turned 19, didn't attract much attention as he walked along the busy London street one afternoon in November 1909. The borough of Islington was packed with the usual miscellaneous collection of Saturday people. It was the heyday of the Empire, the afterglow of the Edwardian age and Britain was at its peak. Many thousands of the stalwart young men who thronged the streets were to spend their youth and their blood in a few years in the muddy fields of Flanders; but at that time the Empire was still supreme. Britain had hope, God was in his Heaven, and all was well with the world.

The tall young man with a great shock of dark brown hair, wide shoulders and flashing grey eyes walked with a confident stride and turned into the old Barnsbury Hall, the local social centre. He quickly made his way to a dusty room on the first floor from whence two men stood in the window and watched, as he came towards the hall.

"That's our young Michael?" said Dr Ryan inquiringly. "Aye" said Sam.

Sam Maguire was the dynamo of the London-Irish, and Chief Steward of the Gaelic Athletic Association, later to give his name to the All Ireland football trophy. There were a dozen other men in the room, and as young Michael came through in the door and took his place, the Chairman rapped on the table.

"Brothers, this meeting of the London Centre commences with an introduction of a new Brother, Brother Michael Collins, who comes well recommended from Dennis Lyons in Cork, a member of our Council, and Brother Michael is well known to you from other activities."

There was a hum of interest from the other men in the room as the sturdy young man walked up to the top table and placed his hand upon the Bible.

"I call upon you, Michael, to take the Oath of the Brotherhood knowing full well its meaning, and knowing full well the consequences should you fail us."

The young man breathed deeply and in a clear firm voice, heavy with a West Cork brogue took the fateful step.

"In the presence of God, I Michael Collins, do hereby solemnly swear that I will do my utmost to establish the National Independence of Ireland, that I will bear true allegiance to the Supreme Council of the Irish Republican Brotherhood, and the Government of the Irish Republic, now virtually established, that I will implicitly obey the Constitution of the Irish Republican Brotherhood, and all my superior officers, and preserve, inviolate the secrets of the Organisation. So help me God!"

Dr Ryan formally shook his hand and there was a slight ripple of applause from the other members. Then Sam Maguire spoke.

"Brothers, having welcomed our new Brother, we must review the business and the work of the Brotherhood in the past year and we must lay out our guidance roles for the next year. I feel in my bones that great events are moving towards a conclusion and that in a few short years we will once again be faced with the opportunity of striking a deadly blow and bringing about that which is our fondest hope."

For the next hour the meeting discussed various matters to advance the interests of the Brotherhood, in particular the development of the Gaelic Athletic Association. Sam Maguire proposed that the new Brother, Michael Collins, would be made treasurer of the London County Board and this would introduce him to a wide area of London-Irish. Arrangements were made accordingly. A number of other decisions were made regarding language classes to be held in four London Boroughs, to which the IRB was instrumental in ensuring good teachers. There was also an Irish dancing class. Various political contacts were discussed and a brief outline of relationships between the Irish Parliamentary Party and the Liberal Government was given by Dr Ryan.

"The Brotherhood", he said, "has little faith in either, but we will keep our lines of communications open and watch carefully what is happening them. At least the Tories are out and as long as this happens there is a chance of using the leverage of the Irish vote to bring about political change and to weaken the link between Britain and Ireland. But in the end as we well know the British must be faced by armed resistance before we can ever win freedom. The lesson of history is that England only ever yields to armed force, never to the claims of justice or truth."

Michael listened intently without comment and stored it all in his mind.

After the Islington meeting was over, the two men, Maguire and Ryan, watched through the dusty window as young Michael strode down the street again.

"What do you think of our new recruit?" Maguire nodded, "I have a feeling that he is like an arrow pointed at the heart of the Empire. He'll do great deeds when the time comes. I must drop a note to Dennis Lyons."

As Michael walked through the bustling crowds in the descending evening gloom , his mind was busy reviewing the afternoon, the decision and step that he had taken in committing himself so irrevocably to the Revolution in Ireland.

As a boy he had lived a happy and carefree childhood in West Cork, not far from Clonakilty, amongst Carbery's Hundred Isles. And there he had immersed himself in the history and the knowledge and the culture of the area, which he absorbed like a sponge, particularly from the local schoolmaster,

Dennis Lyons. In the evenings after school and at the weekends he would often go to the local blacksmith, James Santry.

He would stand there, busy pushing the bellows and watching the sparks fly and hammering on the anvil as the hot steel was forged. Santry would tell of his father and his grandfather and of the people in the area. He was a great storyteller and his own background was a foundation which impressed the young lad. Santry's father had forged pikes for the Fenian rebels in 1848 and 1867, and his grandfather, also a blacksmith, had made pikes for the 1798 rebels. Michael was proud of his association with this broad huge man, of such staunch and direct loyalty. He was himself virgin metal, being formed and forged by Santry's hammer, and the pointed and stirring tales of wars and fighting men.

When he emigrated, at the age of 16, to join the Post Office in London, a traditional slot for West Cork emigrants, he was already committed to the political cause on which his life was channelled. He lodged with his sister, Hannie, also a Post Office sorter, and threw himself into the social activities of the London-Irish, particularly the hurling and football clubs. He was soon made Secretary of the local G.A.A. club, the London Geraldines, and his acerbic and laconic reports on games and the general activities of the club, make interesting reading.

One enduring memory of his boyhood in West Cork, often recurred to Michael's questing mind. It was an adventure towards the end of a long hot summer, and he had just turned 14. At that time, and for several years before, he had been very enthusiastically involved in the life along Carbery's Hundred Isles and all along the sea shore from Baltimore to Ballydehob and then to Schull. It was only a short distance on his bicycle, from his home in Sams Cross to the shore lines where many of his father's relatives had fishing boats, living partially as farmers and fishermen along the coast, and in the River Ilen and in the various islands in Roaring Water Bay.

This particular day he had gone to Baltimore and scrambled over with his bicycle to the head half a mile below the town, past the little cove where the Algerian pirates had once landed, and out by the great beacon to a ledge of rock running out into a deep pool, where he often fished for pollack and rock bream. As he threw his bicycle down beside the rock and started to untangle his line, he heard a loud, terrifying scream. Tumbling up, he went to the edge of the rock and looked out to sea. There, in an old boat about 20 yards offshore, he saw a tall youth, slighter in build than he, but several years older. He had lost his oars and the old boat was rapidly being broken against an isolated ledge of rock, as the surf pounded up and down.

But to the youth's horror, the danger did not appear to be the rock, or drowning in the sea, but in the large pool between him and the shore where Michael stood, clearly emerging above the water was a large fin, and underneath the long torpedo shaped body, longer than his boat, of a great basking shark. Michael was very familiar with these monsters, having seen many in the reaches of the sea from Roaring Water Bay to the Fastnet Rock. He realised immediately that the great fish presented absolutely no danger to the youth. These are harmless vegetarian fish who live entirely on plankton, despite their huge bulk, and although this fish weighed three or four tons, it presented no threat whatsoever. Boys of his age called them, somewhat disparagingly, "Sea-Cows."

The terrified boy in the boat did not know this, and his boat was sinking. Michael hurried down to where the rock joined the shore and pausing only to kick off his shoes, he jumped in and swam with steady strokes across the rock pool towards the boy in the boat. He passed within six feet of the great shark as it was turning slowly to head for open sea. It had no malevolent intention, and it gave a passing glance with it's large mild eyes, like inquisitive soup-plates and then continued on its slow and majestic way towards the sea. Michael quickly reached the boat, as the gunnel came level with the water, and the boy in the boat clasped him firmly around the neck with a cry of joy. Michael turned him on his back, and with swift steady strokes had him ashore within minutes. After a few minutes in the sunshine the boy's courage returned and he sat up, smiling cheerfully at Michael and said

"Hi, what's your name?"

"Michael Collins, I'm from Sams Cross."

"I'm John Charteris."

He had an Anglo-Irish Ascendancy accent.

"I live round the way."

Michael said:

"Let's get our clothes dry, and we'll talk about it after."

He knew that only 50 yards down the shore, was a small cave, about ten feet back into the cliff, which had a dry floor. He had frequently left gear and fish on previous occasions. He led the way there, and soon he and the boy had stripped off their clothes and wrung out the water from them, leaving them to dry across the rocks in the mouth of the cave. In the meantime, they exchanged their life stories.

Michael observed with some respect that the boy, having recovered his confidence, seemed to have no fear whatever of the circumstances they were in. He gathered some dry seaweed and leaves from the back of the cave and small chips of brushwood and driftwood. Michael said "It would be great to have a fire, but we have no matches." The boy smiled mysteriously and produced from his pocket a hemispherical glass. He said "I have a burning lens here from my old boyscout days." He implied that he was above these childish pursuits, these days.

Within minutes he had concentrated the sun on the heap of tinder and soon a wisp of smoke indicated that the temperature was rising, followed in a short time by a tongue of flame. Soon they had a good fire going and they sat in front of it.

They became firm friends during the rest of that long, warm summer and explored each other's minds and backgrounds with avidity. John was at school in England and was full of the doings of himself and his friends and they exchanged many stories. On almost every evening afterwards during the long holiday, they met and rambled, before John had to go back to school. John's father was a brigadier in the army, and always away on service somewhere, and Michael had to prepare himself for his eventual examination into the Civil Service and entry into the London Post Office. John was somewhat reticent about his father's position, but mentioned off-handedly that he was an officer in military intelligence, which was something of a family tradition. "There's been a Charteris in the Army since Culloden", he said. Michael said that his sympathies were with the Jacobite Rebels on that day, but John said that it didn't matter.

He was of a deeply romantic nature, a voracious reader, mainly of adventure stories in which stalwart young Britons explored the wilderness, subdued lesser breeds and fought against fearful odds, for the ashes of their fathers and the temples of their Gods.

He was somewhat worried about Michael's stalwart nationalism, the fruit of his upbringing and feared that it might force them into antagonism in their adult years. He was then almost four years older, and taking stock of his future.

"Michael, did you ever think that we might not always be able to be friends"?

"No – why wouldn't we?"

"Well, my father and his father before him had always served the Empire. Next year I enter Sandhurst to follow in their footsteps. You are a very strong Fenian and have no time for the Empire".

"No matter, the world is big. You'll be in Africa beating the shit out of the blacks. I'll be in Cork beating the shit out of the Brits."

John was not completely satisfied, and they returned to this theme several times.

One event particularly stuck in Michael's mind. On the last evening before they went their separate ways for the school year, John said very gravely:

"You know Michael, you saved my life."

"Ah no." said Michael. "Sure the shark wouldn't have looked towards you."

"He would have killed me, I can't swim. You brought me back and it was 40 feet deep."

"Ah sure, 'twas nothing, 'twas nothing."

"No Michael, you saved my life, you are my brother now, my blood brother. Come, let's make a proper ceremony of it. We will be blood brothers forever."

"What do you mean?"

John gazed into the little fire, and he pulled out his penknife, opened it up.

"I'll tell you", he said.

He held the blade in the flame for a long moment to sterilise it, then he turned and took his right thumb and sliced a small cut about a half an inch in

Michael Collins and the Irish Republican Brotherhood

the side of his thumb. "Now", he said. "Michael, you do the same." Half amused, half wondering, Michael cut his thumb too.

"Now, my brother. Press your thumb against mine, as we take the oath together and mingle your blood with mine, and we will be blood brothers forever. This is what they always do, the fur traders, the great hunters, all the people I have read about in books in the past."

They solemnly pressed their thumbs together and their blood mingled, and John said:

"Now, I, John Charteris, and you, Michael Collins, blood brothers, now and forever, always to take each other's side against the world. Michael, you saved my life once, maybe some time I will save yours."

John said that this was the Brotherhood Oath of Alexander the Great and Ptolemy, when they were both boys in Macedon, and Alexander became the Emperor of the World and Ptolemy became King of Egypt. Each boy intoned the words of the oath in turn, Michael a little self-consciously.

"Your enemies will be mine and mine yours until we die; we will never take up arms against each other, even if our own kin are at war. If I die in a strange land, you will give me my rites, and so I will do for you."

John spat on his thumb and rubbed it across a carboned stick. "Michael, you do the same, and this little scar will be our secret sign and covenant."

Michael, somewhat embarrassed by his intensity, did likewise. They sat together in silence for a long moment, shoulders touching. Young Michael looked across the sea, dusk slowly falling over the Atlantic, unwilling to break the spell of the moment, and nodded half seriously and half amused. Far away, down the arches of the years, the British Empire felt a tremor of foreboding.

The next year, and the year after, when the boys met and clasped hands for the first time, they pressed their thumbs together in a secret sign, unknown to all the rest of the World and John was indeed to save Michael's life, from Ptolemy's Cairo, ten years later.

TWO

Conspiracy

The organisation to which young Michael Collins was sworn in as a member on that November day in 1909 had a long and chequered history. Formally established in 1858, on St Patrick's Day, simultaneously in America by John O'Mahony, and in Ireland by James Stephens, the "Wandering Hawk", it followed the paths of early revolutionary organisations in Europe, conspiratorial, riddled with spies, and ultimately ineffective.

The Irish branch of the Brotherhood was inaugurated at a meeting in Langan's timber yard, in Cork Street, Dublin, presided over by Stephens, a civil engineer. Others present included Thomas Clarke Luby, son of a Protestant merchant and a graduate of Trinity, Joe Denieffe, a tailor, and Garrett O'Shaughnessy, a fitter, also Peter Langan, timber merchant. The organisation was to spread rapidly. Stephens was a messianic and hypnotic character, with enormous energy and single mindedness. Amongst his chief lieutenants was Jeremiah O'Donovan Rossa of West Cork, a boyhood hero of Michael Collins, from the nearby town of Skibbereen.

The core of the Brotherhood remained in the U.S., operating through a popular front organisation called Clan na Gael. Following the wave of European revolutions in 1848, a crop of secretive revolutionary organisations had flourished for a generation or two, with varying degrees of failure. The Fenian Brotherhood or The Irish Republican Brotherhood, as it was called, was the Irish equivalent, and soon achieved strong membership in Ireland and in America and had quite a few members throughout Britain. Many schoolteachers were members and the teacher who had schooled young Michael Collins at Lisnavard, Dennis Lyons, was a member of the Council of the Brotherhood.

Over the years, the IRB had planned many campaigns in Britain, some daring prison escapes and armed raids, but were most effective when they contributed their many talents and intellectual abilities to organising in the cultural, educational and artistic fields, working to restore dignity to the Irish race, and a develop a questioning attitude to counter the inferiority complex of the supporters of the Empire.

The message of revolution for liberty was spread throughout Ireland, by all kinds of wandering pedlars, schoolmasters, by intellectuals and writers, by many sturdy farmers and gradually the movement grew. It was organised in ten or twelve centres linked together and this pyramid layer would spread all over the country. At the very top was the Head Centre, or the C.O.I.R., the Central Organiser of the Irish Republic, who was James Stephens. There was also a Supreme Council with representatives of each county, and an executive, consisting of the head centre, the secretary and the treasurer.

Because of the conspiratorial atmosphere in which the executive of the Brotherhood met, it gradually became divorced and detached from reality in their own minds. The principals believed that the Republic was visible in the distance, merely needing to be uncovered. There would be one hard battle with the Crown and in the meantime, the Central Organiser, the Head Centre of the Fenian Brotherhood, was President of the Republic, now virtually established. There was little control of the enormous sums of money that the movement obtained and of course, lack of control led to corruption.

In some ways, the secret constitution of the brotherhood militated against success, and at least in one significant Article, it laid the foundation for much acrimony and a wounding civil war. The Constitution stated:

> "The Supreme Council of the Irish Republican Brotherhood is hereby declared in fact as well as in right the sole Government of the Irish Republic. Its enactments shall be the laws of the Irish Republic, until Ireland secures absolute national independence, and a permanent Republican government is established.
>
> The President of the Irish Republican Brotherhood is in fact as well as by right the President of the Irish Republic. He shall direct the working of the Irish Republican Brotherhood subject to the control of the Supreme Council."

This was a harmless piece of fictional morale-rousing in the early stages. Later, when there was an elected Dáil Éireann, and a Ministry, responsible to it, the bitter seeds of fratricidal conflict were nurtured.

There was a major split within the American Fenian Brotherhood, the majority of whom embarked on a scheme to invade Canada and detach it from the Crown, and to use that as a base for an Irish invasion. Naturally, the American Government couldn't stand for this and although two invasions were actually made, they were crushed by joint action by the US and Britain. A deep and lasting split occurred in the ranks of the Brotherhood and stultified almost all their activity from its inception right up to the time of Michael's joining.

Peter Beresford Ellis, a respected historian, has written of this Canadian invasion, and its consequences:

> "This invasion involved a deployment of 24,000 Irish veterans of the American Civil War, attacking in three prongs over the Border into the provinces of the then British North America, with artillery and three ex-US Navy warships in support. There was no such entity as the Dominion of Canada then. The aim of the IRB was to seize a salt-water port on the St Lawrence and a territory in Quebec, to use as a bargaining pawn

in negotiations to win Irish independence. The IRB also had links with the revolutionary Parti Rouge, seeking independence for Quebec."

This was a grave threat to British interests in North America, and they reacted promptly and effectively on the political, military and diplomatic fronts. Beresford Ellis records:

"The result was that on May 22, 1867, the British North America Act was given Royal Assent, and the Provinces of Upper and Lower Canada, with Nova Scotia and New Brunswick became the Dominion of Canada. The Premier of New Brunswick admitted that without the IRB invasion, the Union of the Canadian Provinces would never have happened and was a fearful British reaction to the invasion.

The other result was that the British Government was so concerned about its imminent success that a week after the IRB crossed the Canadian border, Britain agreed to pay the United States $15 million in war reparations for their support for the Southern Confederacy, provided President Johnson used US troops to halt the invasion. The British also gave up claims to several territories in the North-West, which subsequently became part of the United States. Incidentally, IRB forces under Colonel John O'Neill defeated British troops in two engagements on the Niagaran peninsula."

The Brotherhood's most creative and fruitful activities had been directed towards national awareness, reviving the spirit of pride and respect for Irish culture. They were the moving spirits behind the creation of the Gaelic Athletic Association in 1884, and the Gaelic League in 1893. In every association and co-operative everywhere, there was an active and eager IRB thinker who practised the creation of cover front organisations, fellow travellers, and infiltration, decades before communism.

To them, almost entirely, could be attributed the enormous rise of the Gaelic Athletic Association, the G.A.A., which by the end of the nineteenth century was the largest amateur association in the world, with an enormous number of its members actually participating in field sports. There were thousands of teams in the association in contrast to sportsmen in other countries, the vast majority of whom went to watch team matches. Until the inception of the GAA, the only team sporting activities in Ireland were soccer, cricket, rugby and hockey, soon to be characterised as "garrison games", and they were a channel and a medium through which the ideology of the Empire was spread among the middle class Irish youth.

The IRB were eager supporters of literary rebellion in Ireland, of the cultural revival, particularly of the spread of the language, which was regarded as an important bastion in the struggle. Much Irish had been lost 50 years before, when the Famine struck the spirit from Ireland, and those who survived the Famine realised that the future of their children depended on being able to speak English. The IRB set out to reverse that defeat and at least make the country bilingual again. They operated through the medium of the Gaelic League, to which they gave direction and purpose. They always promoted respectable "front" figures – a parish priest or a solicitor but the secretary of the branch was usually a member of the IRB, willing and able to do the necessary 'humdrum' work.

The Brotherhood always had newspapers, some public, some secret, to expound its philosophy. Frequently they were suppressed, in the never-ending battle between the Castle and their fiercest antagonists in the polemic over the Republic and the Empire. One such journal was *The Irish People*, with an office in Parliament Street in Dublin. This paper was suppressed in 1866, with its entire editorial staff being arrested and charged with treason-felony. The staff included Thomas Clarke Luby, Charles Kickham, author of *Knocknagow*, John O'Leary, O'Donovan Rossa, and a young sub-editor named James O'Connor.

We will meet Mr O'Connor again in this chronicle. He remained a member of the Brotherhood, for the rest of his rather eventful life. He served a prison sentence of five years for treason-felony, then resumed his career as a journalist. He became a Member of Parliament for West Wicklow, under the "New Departure" development, wherein the separate strands of Fenianism, the constitutional parliamentary party, and the Land Agitation merged with fleeting success until derailed by the Parnell\Kitty O'Shea divorce case. O'Connor married, and had six daughters, the youngest of whom, Moya, was to loomed large in Michael Collins' life and who bore him two children. The O'Connors lived at 2 St. John's Terrace, Blackrock, quite near the foreshore at Seapoint, and Charles Kickham lived with them until his death in 1882.

From its inception, the Brotherhood had a rival in the campaign to enlist the sympathies of the Irish people. Broadly, it can be called the Constitutional Movement, focusing as it did upon constitutional agitation and representation in the Westminster Parliament, from about 1870, since the young protestant landowner, Isaac Butt, had founded the Home Rule Party in the House of Commons. It was a hard fight and they were treated with contempt by the Liberal Party and the Conservatives, the seesaw which formed the British Government. Twenty eight bills introduced by them between 1870 and 1880, with the objective of improving affairs in Ireland were rejected. However, they did take tentative steps in the process of parliamentary obstruction.

Meanwhile, back in Ireland, an IRB man, an ex-Fenian prisoner, Michael Davitt, organised a defensive campaign for people who were thrown out of their homes and farms. The campaign, known as the Land War, opened in 1879 and spread rapidly throughout the west and less rapidly through the rest of the Country. By 1880 the political atmosphere began to heat up, and Davitt and his Land League became powerful forces throughout the country. The rank and file of the IRB supported them, although the leaders had considerable suspicions and reservations, and the Home Rule Party in the House of

Commons had accepted a new leader, Charles Stewart Parnell, a young Protestant landowner from Co. Wicklow.

Soon these three welded together to become a powerful national force of resistance. Parnell was a man of extraordinary gifts. He disciplined the Party and he won the love and allegiance of the people. He became President of the Land League, It was the first time that there was a marriage between the Constitutional movement, operating within the confines of the British Parliament, and of the non-violent civil disobedience movement, and the militant, always eager, members of the Brotherhood. This union of like minds became known as the "New Departure", and provided the most formidable threat to British power in Ireland since the Flight of the Earls.

There were no qualms whatsoever about resorting to violence, if it was possible to advance the movement. Parnell's policy was not to ally the Irish Party to either the Liberal or Conservative Party, but to hold the balance of power and extract a price for each vote and his price was normally support for Home Rule. It also included extending the franchise to take in people without the property qualifications of the original, very limited, Emancipation Act. He went through the Franchise Act of 1884 and trebled the number of persons entitled to vote in Ireland. At that time Parnell was supporting the Conservative Ministry, which came into office the following year. The leader of the Conservatives, Joseph Chamberlain, described the condition of Ireland as worse than that of Poland under the Tsars.

Two years later, in 1886, the Liberal Leader, Gladstone, introduced a Bill to give Ireland a measure of Home Rule. The Conservative and Unionist Parties reacted with utmost hostility. Lord Randolph Churchill went to Belfast to declare that the Orange card was the card to play. Following an enormous Unionist demonstration there was a pogrom in which many Catholics were killed and hundreds of houses burned. The Home Rule Bill was defeated and Parliament dissolved.

The Irish returned 86 members in the subsequent election. The Conservative Party was returned to power and Lord Randolph became Prime Minister. He died a few years later. The Conservatives made many efforts to get rid of Parnell and the enormous embarrassment he was causing, internationally, and within the structures of British Politics, with his policy of disruption. Through the *Times* newspaper, they bought forged letters from a man called Piggott for the sum of £2,500. These letters alleged that Parnell had condoned the Phoenix Park murders of Lord Cavendish and Burke in 1882. A Parliamentary Commission of Inquiry discovered that the letter was a forgery. This discovery was promptly followed by the 'suicide' of Piggott.

At this time, Parnell's secretary was a young, capable and immensely traitorous gentleman, Tim Healy. In 1890, a divorce case was taken against Parnell by the husband of his mistress, Kitty O'Shea. He did not defend the case and Tim Healy led the Irish Party in a vicious attack on their Leader, whom he had described previously as the 'Uncrowned King of Ireland'. The country was immediately divided; the Catholic Bishops and the majority of the clergy supporting Healy, Parnell backed by the majority of the people. Healy was to be the most durable and corrupt of Irish politicians, although almost universally despised, and lampooned as "the bitterest tongue in Ireland", his career spanned 40 lucrative years, during all of which time he faithfully served the Empire in the centre of Irish politics.

Parnell begged that if they were to throw him over, at least they must get their price from the Tories. A Home Rule Bill passed, not just promised! Remember 'Perfidious Albion': The party betrayed him and in December 1890 a non-entity named Justin McCarthy became leader and they dismissed Parnell. He died in the following year at the age of 45. His price had not been paid.

The Home Rule Bill of 1893 was passed by the Commons but was rejected by the Lords. It was the end of constitutional agitation for 20 years. But the Brotherhood continued to grow. They were not based upon the popularity or personality of a politician, but upon the bitter necessities of a prostrate Ireland.

In 1904, a Dublin journalist called Arthur Griffith wrote articles on the resurrection of Hungary. It detailed how Hungary had won independence from the dual-monarchy by refusing to send members to the imperial parliament in Vienna and by civil disobedience of any right of that parliament to legislate for them. The following year he founded a tiny political party, with very little influence. It was called Sinn Féin. It was noted by the Brotherhood as one more factor in the situation, but they did not give a great deal of attention as it did not seem to be of any importance. However, to be on the safe side, the First National Council of Sinn Féin included a Dublin Solicitor, Henry Dixon, also a member of the Supreme Council of the Irish Republican Brotherhood.

In 1909, a striking personality called Countess Constance Markievitz, born Constance Gore-Booth in Sligo, founded a boy scout movement in Ireland, Fianna Éireann, and Liam Mellowes of Galway became it's first organiser. These boys camped, marched and drilled throughout the country and they became insatiable readers of Irish heroic tales. Mellowes was a member of the IRB. In Dublin, Tom Clarke, broken in health but not in spirit by his 15 years of brutal treatment in British prisons, became a dominant personality in the Supreme Council of the IRB. His chief aide was a young man called Sean MacDermott. At this stage the active membership of the Brotherhood was about 2,000, but it could be said that each member could influence almost another thousand.

At the time young Michael Collins joined the IRB, they were anticipating an increased tempo of change in Ireland. By 1910, the political temperature was rising again and things were moving. In January that year, Griffith's paper, *Sinn Féin*, had a prophecy that was justified in the event. The Irish Parliamentary grouping had maintained a representation of 103 men in Westminster for 108 years; 103 Irishmen were faced with 567 foreigners.

Griffith's prophecy was; "Ten years hence the majority of Irishmen would marvel that they once believed that the proper battleground was one chosen and filled by Ireland's enemies".

The election of 1910, returned the Liberals to power. But their majority was so small that the Government called another election before the end of the year and this time put the question of Irish Rule in the forefront of its pro-gramme. The result of the second election was that the Liberals were returned to power with the help of Labour Members, with 314 votes. The Conserva-tive Party numbered 271 and the 84 Irish Nationalists had the balance of power.

There was fury and fear in the ranks of the Orange Lodges. In December they issued a statement calling on all Orange Brothers, in the event of Home Rule becoming law, willing to take active steps to resist its enforcement, to enrol. Next year, the Parliament Act was passed, restricting the veto from the House of Lords so that any bill receiving a third reading would be presented for the Royal Assent, and become law not withstanding the veto of the Lords.

John Redmond, by then Leader of the nationalist Irish Party in Parlia-ment, believed that the last barriers had been overthrown and they would see an Irish parliament in Dublin before the end of 1913. His celebrations were premature.

The Unionists and Conservatives organised to destroy Home Rule and they had no intention of confining the struggle to the House of Commons. Their leader was an extremely capable Dublin solicitor, Sir Edward Carson, a member of the Privy Council and MP for Trinity College. The campaign that Carson launched was not only against the Bill or against Parliament, but in fact, it was against the entire structure of democratic responsibility and they made it clear that if they did not get their way by peaceful means, they would resort to violence. On September 23 1911, at Craigavon, home of Captain James Craig, an enormous demonstration of over 100,000 Orangemen took place. Two days later, the Ulster Unionist Council began preparations to con-stitute a Provisional Government. This body was to be ready to take over the Government of Ulster, by force, should Home Rule come into operation.

By the beginning of 1912, it looked as if the Irish Parliamentary Party in Westminster controlled completely the decisions of the British political ma-chine. The Liberal Prime Minister, Asquith, introduced the Home Rule Bill that everyone was expecting. A great meeting was held in Dublin on the eve of the introduction of the Bill. John Redmond spoke. A young school teacher named Padraic Pearse also spoke. He was a member of the Council of the Brotherhood. His words were measured and pregnant; he spoke in Irish be-cause he would only speak, quite deliberately, to those who would know and understand and be prepared to follow. He said:

> "I'm not accepting the Bill in advance. We may have to refuse it. We are only here to say that the voice of Ireland must be listened to hencefor-

ward. Let us all unite and win a good Act from the British. I think it can be done. But take note, that if we are tricked this time, there is a Party in Ireland, and I am one of them, that will advise the Irish to have no further dealing with the foreigner for ever again but to answer to them henceforward with a strong hand and a sword edge. Let the foreigner understand that if we are cheated once more there will be red war in Ireland."

The next day, Asquith, the Liberal Leader, introduced the Government of Ireland Bill, its terms this day made public for the first time. The Bill proposed to establish an Irish Parliament, consisting of the King and two Houses, a Senate of 40 members and a Council of 164. The Head of the Irish Executive would be appointed by the King and would be the Lord Lieutenant, not appointed by Parliament, Irish ministers were to be appointed by the Lord Lieutenant, and he would nominate the 40 members of the Senate. He was also to appoint all judges. The overall authority of the British Parliament was retained. It had the sole right to make laws connected with foreign relations, marine affairs, peace and war, and treaties and all major aspects of national sovereignty. It had full power over customs and excise and full control of taxation. The supreme authority of the British Parliament would remain unaffected and undiminished and at the same time the number of Irish representatives at Westminster would be reduced from 103 to 42. Overall, the Bill was a fraud and a sham.

Despite this, it was opposed by the Unionists and the Orange element in the North as if it meant real freedom. The blatant bigotry enshrined in the very culture of the Orange community couldn't tolerate the possibility of the "lesser breeds without the law" having a Parliament, even one that had no powers at all.

Redmond foolishly prattled on that it was the answer to the nationalist dream and a full and final settlement. There was disgust and rejection in nationalist circles in Dublin. The Home Rule Bill passed it's second reading on 9 May with a majority of over 100. The next day pogroms started in Belfast. The Orangemen attacked the great shipyard and drove out 2,000 Catholic workmen. In the end, many houses were burned and a number of Catholics were killed.

On 28 September, a solemn League and Covenant was drawn up by Lord Londonderry, Sir Edward Carson and Captain Craig and it was signed by over 220,000 people. The day of the signing was observed throughout Ulster as a public holiday. Union Jacks were flown and special religious services were held. And these men, loyal Ulster subjects of King George V signed an undertaking "To stand by one another and using all means that might be found necessary to defeat the present conspiracy to set up a Home Rule Parliament in Ireland and in the event of such a Parliament being forced upon us, we further solemnly and mutually pledge ourselves to refuse to recognise it's authority." The IRB was not going to have it all its own way.

Later that month, every able-bodied man in Ulster, who had signed the Covenant, was called upon to enrol for either political or military service against Home Rule and the Ulster Volunteer Force was formed. The sinister initials, UVF, first appeared on gable walls at this time. The armed conspiracy to mount a rebellion against the Crown was led by a member of the Privy Council, Sir Edward Carson, top lawyer in the United Kingdom and supported by Bonar Law, the Leader of the Conservative and Unionist Party in Westminster. Asquith, then Liberal Premier, described it as "furnishing the complete grammar of anarchy."

On 1 January, Sir Edward Carson moved the exclusion of the Province of Ulster from the Home Rule Bill. All nine counties were to be excluded from the operation of the Home Rule Act. Bonar Law supported him and declared that the Ulster Unionists would prefer to accept the Government of a foreign country rather than accept Home Rule. In Germany, this sentiment was noted with keen interest by the advisors of the Kaiser. Carson's amendment was defeated but in order to get his majority, Asquith had made a deal and in the course of the debate he announced that before the Bill would become law, another general election must be held. This was a total surrender to the course of anarchy which he had denounced a month before. The Bill passed its final reading in January with a majority of 110, to be rejected by the Lords. And then it went through the charade of two more sessions in the Commons. It finally passed its second reading and became law on 9 June 1913.

Throughout that summer, the Unionists organised themselves for rebellion. On 24 September, the Ulster Unionist Council, without bothering to call an election, declared itself to be the central authority of the Provisional Government, the first of many provisional movements in Ireland this century. Sir Edward Carson became Chairman of the Central Authority and Prime Minister designate, and other members included Captain Craig, the Duke of Abercorn and the Marquis of Londonderry. War funds were quickly gathered and emissaries were sent to Germany. A determined, and extremely successful effort, was made to subvert the loyalty of the generals and senior officers in the Army, both in Ireland and in England An early enthusiastic advocate of their cause was General Sir Henry Wilson, later Field Marshal and Chief of the Imperial General Staff. In the middle of August, Sir Edward Carson met the Kaiser for lunch in Hamburg.

The IRB Council was watching intensely as the loyalists staked out the path of armed rebellion against the Crown. In his weekly journal, Padraic Pearse wrote: 'Personally, I think the Orangeman with a rifle is a much less ridiculous figure than a Nationalist without a rifle.' In August that year, war broke out in Dublin – class war. The attempt of the Dublin employers to smash the Irish Transport and General Workers Union led to a strike that brought extreme poverty and deprivation to many thousands in Dublin. The police were brutal, frequently banning meetings and unashamedly taking sides on behalf of the employers. In October, Larkin, the leader of the ITGWU, addressed an immense meeting in Dublin and there with the support of a protestant Ulsterman, Captain Jack White, he called upon the workers of Dublin to form a Citizen Army in their own defence which could be capable of repelling the RIC. The response was enthusiastic. James Connolly became the first Chief of Staff. In the spring of 1914, the strike ended in failure, but the Citizen Army remained as a growing force, and Connolly in particular and the small group of its officers whom he influenced began to develop their thoughts on the topic of revolutionary warfare.

Earlier, in October 1913, the Council of the IRB found the opportunity to propose a National Irish Volunteer Body. The opportunity was an article published in the Gaelic League organ by Professor Eoin McNeill. A provisional committee under McNeill's chairmanship was formed. The Committee at the launch of the Volunteer Movement included some prominent members of the IRB Council, Padraic Pearse, Sean MacDermott and Bulmer Hobson. The inaugural meeting of the Volunteers took place on 25 November in the Rotunda. The Fianna Éireann organisation provided stewards in green uniform and the huge crowd overflowed the Concert Hall into the grounds. An outdoor meeting of several thousand people was held, McNeill being the chairman.

Four thousand men enrolled in the Irish Volunteers at that meeting. Arrangements were made for the hiring of school halls throughout Dublin for the formation of 15 companies in the city and the movement spread like wildfire throughout Ireland. One of the officers of the 6th Battalion was a tall young mathematics teacher named Eamon De Valera.

The guiding spirit behind the whole idea was Tom Clarke but his name appeared nowhere in connection with it and he was not a member of any committee, being a rank and file volunteer. But his colleagues on the Supreme Council of the Brotherhood were watching, promoting and gaining control of the Volunteers throughout the country. By the end of the year, the Volunteers had 10,000 members, and the number was increasing every day.

On the evening of 24 April 1914, a freighter crept along the grey cliffs of the Gobbins, at Islandmagee, Co. Antrim. As the ship emerged from the fog and nosed into the docks at Larne, the RIC barracks, the railway station and all the crossroads were occupied by armed UVF units, without any resistance whatever. Lines of hundreds of motorcars were marshalled into position to receive and distribute the deadly cargo of the *Clyde Valley* – 35,000 German rifles and two and a half million rounds of ammunition.

With the unloading of that poisonous cargo, violence emerged in modern Irish politics. The Orange Order and the Unionist Party, which were indistinguishable, had served notice that they proposed an armed insurrection against the United Kingdom: "We will kick the King's Crown into the Boyne," rather than submit to a democratic decision of Parliament and implement Home Rule.

The news sent a shock of horror throughout the country and spurred the Irish Republican Brotherhood. Later that year, a private yacht, *the Asgard*, owned by Erskine Childers, sailed into Howth with 900 Mausers aboard and another yacht, *the Kelpie*, owned by Conor Cruise O'Brien, carrying 600 guns, later landed at Kilcoole. The Irish Volunteers and the Ulster Volunteer Force squared up to one another. The sudden onset of the Great War in Europe providentially avoided a bloodbath in Ireland, and soon both sets of Volunteers found themselves betrayed by their leaders – Carson and Redmond – and they mingled their blood on the distant battlefields of Flanders and Suvla Bay.

THREE

Love in London

Away from all these activities, the London IRB were very active in organising Gaelic football, hurling, Irish language classes and dancing classes, and into all of these the young vigorous Michael Collins threw himself with great enthusiasm. He became secretary of the London Geraldines football and hurling club. He attended language classes. The few words of Irish he had brought with him from West Cork were greatly reinforced when he set his interest in his studies of the language and within a year he had become quite proficient. The Brotherhood was well organised throughout Britain and particularly on the literary and social side. There were weekly dances and all kinds of social functions to which Collins went, and rapidly became a key person. He had a tall, handsome, vigorous carriage and presence, and he was one of those who were always noticed when they came into a room, no matter how crowded. He became a figure of note and attention by the young girls on the Association fringes. By then he was 19 with abundant energy and had discovered that he had an enormous attraction for the opposite sex and he had little difficulty as a lusty youth in London in penetrating the mysteries of human love.

One night he came to a Grand Ceilidhe and dance in Islington, towards the end of 1910, and there, as he was standing at the bar drinking lemonade, he looked up. A few feet from him, with dazzling blue eyes fringed by a mane of golden hair and a face of extraordinary vitality, stood a tall girl, exquisitely dressed with cream gloves. Michael looked into her eyes. She would be, he thought, five or six years older than him. But then what matter! Older women, and he, were often a mutual challenge.

Sam Maguire was a few steps behind him. He grabbed his elbow and said:

"Come Michael, I must introduce you to this lady." "This is Moya O'Connor". "Moya, this is young Michael Collins from West Cork. He is in the Post Office with us here."

She took off her gloves and he clasped her cool hand, noting half instinctively that on her left hand was a gold wedding ring. Her eyes curled up in a smile.

"O'Connor, that's a Cork name."

"Well", she said, "Not really, Dublin, London, not Cork."

He was lost in her charm. They danced twice, then sat down to chat. Perhaps she was a widow? Who was Mr. O'Connor? He quickly ascertained that she came to this dance once a month, and she went to an Irish class, run by the O'Donovan Rossa Branch every week.

"Well, isn't that a coincidence. I was thinking of joining that class. I need to work on my Irish."

She looked at him speculatively through her long curving eyelashes.

"Is that so? Well, we will possibly meet again there."

"Yes, I hope so." said Michael, half confused; this was a cool one.

He later pumped a grinning Sam Maguire for information about the enigmatic lady, and Maguire's answer intrigued him even more. Her father was a Brother, and an ex-fenian prisoner who has served a sentence on Parkhurst and Dartmoor for treason-felony. She was married to the Solicitor-General in the Liberal Government, Crompton Llewelyn Davies, but she used her maiden name, O'Connor, in Irish circles,

Next Wednesday he enrolled in the O'Donovan Rossa Ard Rang, Senior Class, for speakers who knew some Irish and wished to practice. She was also a member. Inevitably, they spent much time in each other's company, and Michael became infatuated with Moya. Moya and Michael came to be regarded almost as a couple after a short time.

Her husband, Crompton Llewellyn-Davis, was a solicitor with a thriving practice. He was 28 years older than her, and a man of extraordinarily liberal views. His views did not only extend into politics, but to domestic arrangements as well. After a few months Michael and Moya had become lovers.

Crompton Llewellyn-Davis was quite a strange person. He was the son of a Yorkshire parson, and through sheer ability had propelled himself to the top ranks of the legal profession without any money of consequence behind him. In a few years he had earned much as legal advisor to the Liberal Party. Amongst his practice were very many important people, several Indian princes, many politicians and aristocrats, and Lloyd-George.

He had drafted up legislation for the Liberal Government, as a specialist in International law. In 1909 he had become quite wealthy and was made Solicitor-General. He began to look around for a suitable wife to dignify his lifestyle. She must be British and intelligent. He couldn't bear to be with a foreign woman or a stupid woman. His wife would have to be dignified and respectable because of his position. A good wife and hopefully a good mother. Then he chanced upon this charming Irish girl less than half his age. In British terms, they had a whirlwind courtship, and they married after three months. Throughout their entire married life, they were exceptionally close and ideally happy, without any shadow of domestic disharmony, despite her many madcap adventures. They loved each other sincerely, but not exclusively, and they were very good friends. He was always more interested in a woman's mind than her body, and did not have any proprietorial instincts, being a genuine bohemian. His close friends, John and Hazel Lavery, both painters, had the same outlook. The post-Edwardian period in London, the time of Collin's adolescence, was noted for a sexual liberalism and indifference not equalled until the mini-skirt and condom era of the sixties.

There was no jealousy whatever in Crompton's personality, and he became as fond of Michael Collins as he was of Moya, and she loved them both equally. Moya had been reared in Blackrock, Co. Dublin, and her father, James O'Connor, had been a Fenian prisoner, then a Nationalist MP and a staunch Parnellite. Charles Kickham, the staunch old Tipperary Fenian and author of *Knocknagow*, lived his last years in the O'Connor house at St John's Terrace, Blackrock. Her childhood had been blighted by an unusual family tragedy. One day, Moya, her mother and her three sisters went picnicking on the beach at Salthill, close to the West Pier in Dun Laoghaire. They picked mussels and other shellfish off the rocks and ate them, and became very sick. By the next morning, Moya's mother and three sisters were dead and she was the only survivor. The tragic picnic was much commented upon, and James Joyce mentions in *Ulysses*, "poor Man O'Connor, his wife and children poisoned by shellfish on the Salthill shore."

A few years later, O'Connor, to whom she had clung with desperate emotion, married again. His new wife did not like Moya, and Moya hated the interloper. As soon as she reached the age of 18, she went to live with an aunt in London.

Whilst working there, in the civil service, she was introduced to Crompton Llewellyn-Davis. There was an instant warmth of feeling between them. He was a replica of the handsome and friendly father of her lonely teens in Dublin. After a few months, he asked her to marry him and she accepted him without a second thought. He was of a sedentary, almost placid character, and his early lovemaking was dutiful rather than passionate, but he awakened reserves of feeling in her which demanded expression. Then Collins came into her life and awakened a new flowering of emotion; in a short time they had become lovers.

She confided to Crompton that she was becoming very attracted to the turbulent youth from West Cork, who was nine years younger than she. He was disturbed initially, but for her sake. He had no trace of jealousy: "As long as you are sure he would treat you with respect, I don't mind a bit. Invite the lad to dinner next week and we'll run an eye over him. Friday next, John and Hazel Lavery are dining with us and it might be fun to have young Collins along as well."

It was a momentous decision. The dinner party in Crompton's Kensington house the next week marked an important stage in Collins's evolution. Hazel Lavery gazed at him with considerable interest and her eyes sparkled. With the intuition for which she was famous, she realised the nature of the relationship between Collins and Moya, and she determined that she would have a slice of that action.

Hazel Lavery was an extraordinary person, and a typical example of a bohemian, almost amoral, sophisticate. Born Hazel Martyn, of a rich American family, who had made money in beef in Chicago, her mother had taken her, for her own good, away from some of her teenage companions and taken her on a tour of Europe, when she was only 17, her mother, believing, with good reason, that the atmosphere in Chicago was somewhat decadent. Although so young, Hazel was already engaged to a French Canadian, Doctor Trudeau. However, on their trip to France, they stayed in a luxurious hotel in Brittany and Hazel immediately became interested in some other guests. One of them was a tall, aristocratic Irish painter by the name of John Lavery. He had with him a little blond German girl of about 15 who had posed for him in some of his paintings. He also had a male model, being of occasional bisexual tastes. John Lavery was typical of the bohemian painters of that period, totally careless of convention, because of the fact that they were gentlemen, regarding themselves as above the law. Later Lavery wrote, "As when I first met Hazel, and she shared the scandal, if there should be one, of my taking a beautiful young girl to the country, for months at a time. Her mother, Mrs Edward Martyn, was somewhat watchful."

Hazel joined enthusiastically in this bohemian "menage a trois" and her mother became extremely alarmed and wired Doctor Trudeau. He came and took her back to America. Within a short time Hazel and her doctor were married and she had a young daughter, but in less than two years time, she became a widow. She promptly came back to England and pursued John Lavery. She succeeded in ousting his other mistresses, and they became married quite soon after her arrival in London. Hazel was content, having the husband that she wanted, who was a very popular person among London society, but her sexual appetite could not be satisfied with his languid and somewhat erratic lovemaking. Within the next ten years, she had welcomed many of the important men in politics and literature and the arts, both in England and in Ireland, into her generous bed. Her social skills and amorous efforts earned her husband a knighthood, and to her delight, the little Chicago girl became Lady Lavery.

In the spring of 1912 Moya became pregnant, and in December of that year their child was born, Richard Llewllyn Davies, a fine strong boy. There was no doubt that Michael Collins was the father, and the family accepted it as quite a natural happening. The boy came to know of it, as a normal family matter, in his teens, and took it in his stride. The three-cornered love between Moya, Michael and Crompton lasted as long as their lives, and was to have enormous impact on Anglo-Irish relations. The boy, Richard, eventually went to Cambridge, where he was an intimate, in the thirties of the "Apostles", Burgess, McClean, Blunt, Philby, *et al.*

Richard became a leading architect, correspondent, a member of the Labour Party, and eventually Architectural Correspondent of the London *Times*, and a Labour life peer in 1964, as did his wife. He never boasted of his Collins parentage, nor did he make any attempt to hide or deny it. His daughter Melissa, who is a television producer, had thoughts about making a documentary about the Moya and Michael story in the eighties, and Richard at first agreed to help, with a number of family letters between the pair, and extracts from Moya's suppressed journals, but later changed his mind on the grounds that the Irish people would be displeased at anything that might detract from Michael Collin's reputation. I questioned Melissa about this, in January of 1994, and she was firm that her father was anxious to protect Collins from possible criticism. Melissa herself was not convinced of her grand-parentage, being of the opinion that there was no proof in the matter, and Crompton or another man could just as easily have been the father of Richard, not that it mattered. But, Moya seems to have had no doubts whatever.

Michael O'Cuinneagáin, in his book *On the Arm of Time* mentions an informant who:

> "had been in London about 1973 to meet some leading members of the British Labour Party, to discuss happenings in the 'North' . . . they were joined by a member of the House of Lords, and introductions were by way of christian names ... the Lords member was introduced as Richard . . . on a number of occasions Richard called my friend 'Paddy' which irked him somewhat – it was not the name used during the introductions. At a stage, 'Paddy' could refrain no longer and implied that Richard was an insulting English bastard, whereupon Richard retorted sharply "I am as much an Irishman as you – Michael Collins was my father.' Despite 'Paddy's' best endeavours, Richard refused to discuss the matter any further."

Michael and Moya parted temporarily, in 1916, when he returned to Ireland to take part in the Easter Rising, but there exists a voluminous correspondence between them, interrupted by the Rising and his internment in Frongoch, but commencing again after his release, despite his very busy involvement in the national resurgence before 1918. After his death, Moya poured out her grief and love in a poignant journal, publication of which was forcibly suppressed by some of Collin's more strait-laced friends.

She also translated the famous Irish classic *Fiche Bliadhan ag Fás* of life on the Blasket Islands, into English, and the author, Muiris O Suilleabhain, stayed at her house in Furry Park at the time. She helped a number of Collin's friends to write books about the period of the Anglo-Irish War, and somewhat ironically, the best-known of these is *With the Dublin Brigade* by Charley Dalton, which she practically wrote for him.

A second child. Kathleen, was born in 1915. After the death of Collins, the family continued to live in Furry Park, which was left to Kathleen, and Moya later moved to Killadreenan House, in Wicklow. Crompton and the Llewellyn Davies were not treated with any consideration by the new gombeen Irish Government and were in modest hardship for a time. When Richard went to Cambridge, Kathleen stayed on, on her own in Furry Park and was somewhat of a recluse. She was studious and academically gifted, and took a PhD in ancient languages, including Old Irish, perhaps a throwback to Moya's enthusiasm for the language. Finally, when she was 33, she went to Scotland,

and lectured in Edinburgh University for most of her life. She died in the autumn of 1996.

FOUR

Rebellion in Dublin

On the day that War broke out, Collins was in Liverpool, playing in a football match with the London Irish against Liverpool G.A.A. and he used the occasion to attend a meeting of the Liverpool Centre of the IRB, presided over by Neil Kerr. It was important, now that the die had been cast for the European War, that the organisation of the Irish Republican Brotherhood be extended and firmly compacted throughout Britain and Ireland and Collins worked actively in that field for the next year. He changed his job then, leaving the Post Office to become a clerk in a well-known firm of stockbrokers which gave him a great deal of practical instruction in the ways of finance. He was a keen student and read voraciously. The knowledge he acquired he was later to put to very good account as Minister of Finance in the Government of the Irish Republic.

He was regarded with great favour by the London Centre of the IRB, and gradually was promoted, with more and more responsibilities in their ranks. On Christmas in 1915, the IRB sent him over as an emissary to meet the Supreme Council to find out what were the detailed plans of the Brotherhood for action during the War. He had several extended meetings with Tom Clarke and Sean MacDermott and other members of the Council and he returned to London fully briefed on the plans for the Rising. He decided that he would come back to Dublin and be on hand to take an active part when the Rebellion broke out. He applied for a job as secretary of the National Aid Association and also with the accountancy firm of Craig Gardner & Co. On 15 January 1916, he left England. When giving notice to his boss he told him, with his tongue in cheek, that he was leaving to join the Army. His boss was warmly congratulatory, thinking of only one Army, and he gave him a cheque for an extra month's salary. He had an emotional farewell with Moya, spending the night with her in her Kensington home, Crompton being graciously absent on business in Wales.

On the mailboat, Collins had a few drinks in the bar with several British soldiers who congratulated him also when he told them he was coming home to Ireland to enlist. He wondered if he would meet them again, at gunpoint, during the Rising. Collins threw himself into the preparatory work for the Rising, with great enthusiasm, becoming officially a member of the Irish Volunteers and being appointed as Staff Captain and ADC to Tomás MacDonagh, a member of the Military Committee of the council. Political developments speeded up the tempo of events in Ireland.

At the beginning of 1916, the Supreme Council of the IRB was becoming increasingly concerned at the attitude of James Connolly, Commandant of the Irish Citizen Army, the armed wing of the Irish Transport and General Workers Union. He seemed to have lost patience and tolerance for anyone else in the National Movement, whom he regarded with scarcely concealed impatience and contempt. Each week he seemed to make more and radical statements, constantly drilling the Citizen Army with real rifles outside Liberty Hall, field training, and defying the authorities. The Council resolved to tell him the danger involved, and that they were definitely determined to have a Rising and that he must play a disciplined part in it. They were afraid that a spark from him might stir up action from the Government and be the excuse for wholesale repression of the entire Movement.

One Thursday evening, Michael Collins and two other volunteers were picked, all IRB men, to be guards on a house in Kimmage. Connolly was tricked into a meeting with Pearse, McDonagh and Tom Clarke, about the only three men that he respected in the country. He was informed then at that meeting that he was to be put in possession of important military information, that he must swear never to divulge it and that if he did, the consequences for the nation as a whole, would be totally disastrous.

Connolly listened, with polite scepticism verging on mildly-concealed contempt. The IRB and the Volunteer leadership had underestimated the passion of this man. His fury sprang from the long trial of the Dublin workers in the 1913 Strike, and the attitude of the respectable people and the Churches. He writhed at the humiliation and death imposed on his beaten followers when they were compelled by the actions of the Dublin employers to join the British Army in order to feed their families; and they were sent as cannon fodder to the killing fields of Flanders.

"My men were broken in Dublin Town." he said, "But they are buried in Flanders."

He was determined that it would not happen again, not to a single soldier of the Citizen Army. "If we die, we die here, if we fight, we fight here. Not in Suvla Bay, not in Gallipoli, not in those countries." The IRB found him quite difficult to deal with. He was much more determined, much better equipped for argument than they were and much better versed in the history and the reality of what was happening in Europe. They were theorists; he was a practical revolutionary.

The first meeting, which lasted four hours, was inconclusive and he was informed that he must stay there that night and the discussions would be continued the next day and for another two or three days if necessary. They told him that they were determined upon a Rising before the war was over. He challenged them to give him a date and, of course, they couldn't at that stage. He gave his word not to attempt to escape, but nonetheless, Connolly had to put up with the indignity of a young Volunteer, Michael Collins, sleeping in the same room as he and another outside across the door in a campbed.

Collins got little sleep that night. It was the first time he had met Connolly and it was a big start for a short but extremely respectful relationship. He quickly came to appreciate the other man's passion and to love his sincerity. He had little knowledge of or respect for socialist theory at that time, but in the next two days he had a crash course on the workers movement in Europe. The first night Connolly never let him sleep. "The reason we must fight here? We must save the Socialist Movement of Europe from its disgrace and we don't care whether or not you fight with us. We don't care if only a hundred men fight."

Collins couldn't understand the passion behind this and he asked for an explanation. Connolly gave it again:

> "The Second International was the most powerful socialist movement ever. It had millions of members throughout Europe. It had hundreds of members in all the Parliaments of Europe. It had thousands of fulltime officials between the trade unions and the political movement in Germany, France, Britain.
>
> For the past 20 years we have studied the question of war and what would happen to the ordinary people of Europe if war came, and we decided to put the lunatics in prison, a prison in charge of Governments and if their Imperialist manoeuvrings ended in a resort to arms, we would take control and prevent the bloodshed. For the first time in the history of the world, the ordinary people, acting through the Second Socialist International, would take charge and simply refuse to go to war.
>
> We decided to be forceful and we told all Europe so many times that at the signal for mobilisation the railway workers in Europe would strike. We would stop the trains running. We would prevent the armies from mobilising. Our members in the parliaments of the continent would vote against the war and against the governments and prevent monies being allocated to war purposes. We would physically and financially prevent the armies from coming into conflict with each other, in touch with each other even. That was the dream and it was easy to accomplish, all we needed was the political will. The generals and the kings would be helpless without us."

Collins listened spellbound. This man had a dream and it could so easily have been accomplished. Then he continued:

> "Some of the best minds in Europe were involved in this planning, but one in particular above all, one brilliant woman, who was the leader intellectually of us all, a little slip of a woman called Rosa Luxembourg. Yet she was a giant and towered amongst us in power, in personality, in the force of her thought and she hammered this programme through the International. We all pledged that we would accept it and our slogan was

26

'We will turn the Imperialist war into a civil war'."

"What happened?" said Collins.

"What happened was quite simple. Our leaders were traitors. Our leaders were fops with carefully polished words and carefully polished swords, posturing on the stage and when the war came, the members of Parliament in Britain, France and Germany voted to support the War. The trade union leaders instructed their members to stay at their posts, and the trains ran and millions of decent dues-paying working men hurled themselves on one another and started to murder each other in the name of the Kaiser and the King."

Collins was deeply moved by his next words, the key to this passionate man, and they reverberated in his mind for the rest of his years.

"I will make sure it doesn't happen again. It won't happen in Ireland. The first word of conscription of the Irish, the workers of Dublin in the Irish Citizen Army will take Dublin Castle. We will turn their Imperialist War into a Civil War, and it will be the end of the Empire, even if we only start with a hundred men. We have no choice of living or dying, you see, but we do have a choice of how we do it. The ordinary workers of Dublin are poor and without power. We know that we are going to die. We do have the power to decide that we will die here in Dublin, fighting against our real enemies – not in France, killing strange men who have never harmed us."

Collins was sucked into the pool of his enormous conviction, and he never lost his affection and respect for James Connolly. The next day came threats from the Citizen Army conveyed by an angry Countess Markievicz that they would attack the Volunteers if Connolly was not released immediately. However, Connolly had by then been convinced by Clarke and Pearse that they were in earnest, and he agreed to be sworn in to the IRB and accepted a position on the Supreme Council and on the Military Committee, which was to plan the Rising. Peace was restored when he was released and rejoined the Union and the Citizen Army at Liberty Hall.

Collins and Connolly met frequently during the next three tense months, and when the long-promised Rising broke out, Staff Captain Michael Collins was Aide and Adjutant to Commander General James Connolly, O/C Dublin Division of the Army of the Irish Republic, when they stormed the GPO in O'Connell Street.

He was at Connolly's side when the leader was shot in the thigh and ankle by sniper bullets, and worked alongside him, on his stretcher, in the flames and confusion of the burning GPO. He was with Connolly when he was stretchered out through a hole in the wall to Moore Street, and carried up to the Rotunda to surrender, and he wept bitter tears when he heard that the wounded Commandant, strapped to a chair, was carried out for execution at Kilmainham, and gave his blessing to his executioners, and "to all brave men who do their duty."

In May of 1915, Asquith had announced that there would be a Coalition

Government, to prosecute the War. His announcement was greeted with great surprise and interest in Ireland. The formation of the new Cabinet would indicate its intention with regard to the Home Rule Bill, on the Statute Book but under suspension. The new Cabinet, however, included eight Unionists. Bonar Law, Leader of the Conservative and Unionists, became Secretary of State for the Colonies. Walter Long was President of the Local Government Board. The Leader of the Orange rebellion in Ulster, Sir Edward Carson, was made Attorney General with a seat in the Cabinet and Galloper Smith was given the post of Solicitor General. These had been the most reckless and disloyal rebels against His Majesty's Government, the most violent enemies of Home Rule and of parliamentary authority and they had been rewarded with the most influential positions in the gift of the Crown. There was no doubt whatever that constitutional agitation for Home Rule had become a farce, and on 17 September, the date on which the Home Rule Act would have come into operation, orders in Council were promulgated by the Government, suspending the operation of the Act until the end of the war.

This debacle caused great indignation in Ireland, and fatally undermined the influence of the Parliamentary Party and its leader, John Redmond. By contrast, the Volunteers received greater support, both publicly and in membership and the influence of the Revolutionary Brotherhood within the Volunteers was increased as the rank and file understood quite well what their teachings would mean.

Another event occurred in July of that year. In America, the veteran Fenian, Diarmuid O'Donovan Rossa, died and was brought home to Ireland. His part in the long history of the IRB was known, his preparations for the Rising of 1867 and the unspeakable suffering he endured for 15 years in British prisons were known to every schoolchild in Ireland. He bore an honoured name. His coffin lay in State in Dublin City Hall and hundreds of thousands of people thronged to pay homage, marshalled by Volunteers in green uniform. On 1 August, a great multitude followed his hearse to Glasnevin and there Padraic Pearse gave a speech outlining, in the clearest terms, the Fenian programme.

> "It seems right that I should speak here, representing a new generation that has been re-baptised in the Fenian faith and that has accepted the responsibility of carrying out the Fenian programme. Deliberately here, we avow ourselves as he avowed himself in the dock. Irishmen of one allegiance only. We will stand together in brotherly union for the achievement of the freedom of Ireland. We must give Ireland, our love and repay to English rule here in Ireland, our hate. This is a place of peace, sacred to the dead, where men should speak with all charity and all restraint. O'Donovan Rossa held it a Christian thing to hate evil, to hate untruth, to hate oppression and in hating them, to strive to overthrow them. As long as Ireland holds these Fenian graves, Ireland unfree shall never be at peace."

By January of 1916, the Supreme Council of the IRB decided that the Rising would begin on Easter Sunday, 23 April. There were two major organisational problems – the Irish Citizen Army and the non-IRB majority of senior officers in the Volunteers. By then, James Connolly had finally accepted that the IRB were serious and had agreed to mesh the Irish Citizen Army into the Irish Volunteers as soon as the Rising took place.

The greater problem was what to do with the majority of the officers of the Volunteers who were loyal, to McNeill as Chief of Staff; Commandant O'Connell headed an important military sub-committee. Many senior officers including Bulmer Hobson and The O'Rahilly, would be in favour of defensive military action if the Government had attempted to enforce conscription or to disarm the Volunteers but they were not in favour of a military initiative and a rebellion. It was, therefore, necessary to keep these officers in the dark about the preparations made by the IRB members of the Executive for a Rising at Easter. This was the source of a fatal weakness. It couldn't possibly have worked – and it didn't.

In February, the IRB Council informed the Clan na Gael Executive in America of plans for a rising and a request to make diplomatic connections with the German Government. The Germans agreed to have a ship with 20,000 rifles, machine guns and ammunition at Fenit Pier in Tralee Bay. The IRB appointed Pearse Commander in Chief, his appointment kept secret for the time being. He had all the required authority since he was officially Director of Organisation. Sir Roger Casement was at this time involved in the futility of raising an Irish Brigade in Germany and he was not fully conversant with the plans of Clan na Gael or the IRB. He had hoped to have 200,000 rifles and a corps of German officers to land in Ireland. When he discovered that the amount of aid was much smaller, he was in despair. He did his best to cancel or postpone the Rising until he could came back to Ireland.

In the meantime, Eoin McNeill, nominal Chief of Staff of the Irish Volunteers, discovered the plans of the IRB for the Rising, and was outraged. On Easter Sunday, the Rising was to commence under the guise of "Easter Manoeuvres". McNeill placed a prominent advertisement in the *Sunday Independent*, the leading newspaper in the country, announcing the cancellation of the "manoeuvres" and instructing all Volunteers to refrain from all activity. The great majority of the Volunteers obeyed this order, and the country-wide Rising was aborted. Only in Dublin did a small number of the planned actions take place, with less than a quarter of the Volunteers mobilised. McNeill's intervention ensured that the Easter Rising was a military disaster.

There was confusion with dates and pilots, and the German ship, the *Aud*, arrived a day too early, the Council in the meantime, having put back the Rising by one day. Unfortunately, the arms ship did not have wireless and kept the original assignment. No one checked that the message had been received.

Frantically, the Supreme Council of the IRB tried to salvage the situation by scheduling the Rising for the next day. On Easter Monday 1916, Michael Collins marched with his Volunteer Company to take possession of the General Post Office in O'Connell Street. He had just turned 26 and all his life seemed to have been directed towards this moment and he was finally, formally in arms against the enemy. The first day he was too busy to take much impression of all the great things that were happening. As a Staff Officer he was working very closely with James Connolly in preparing the Post Office for defence. There was the constant sound of breaking windows, building barricades and scouring the place for suitable sniper positions and taking the range of rooftops, from which they might themselves come under sniper fire.

Connolly issued orders to the garrison; "From today, there is no longer the Irish Volunteers and the Irish Citizen Army – Only the Army of the Irish Republic."

Pearse read the Proclamation of the Republic in the Portico of the GPO. It remains an interesting document, carefully crafted by the Supreme Council and expressing the essence of the IRB philosophy:

"Poblacht na h-Éireann, The Provisional Government, To the People of Ireland. IRISHMEN AND IRISHWOMEN: In the name of God and of the dead generations from which she receives her old tradition of nationhood, Ireland, through us, summons her children to her flag and strikes for her freedom.

Having organised and trained her manhood through her secret revolutionary organisation, the Irish Republican Brotherhood, and through her open military organisations, the Irish Volunteers and the Irish Citizen Army, having patiently perfected her discipline, having resolutely waited for the right moment to reveal itself, she now seizes the moment and, supported by her exiled children in America and by gallant allies in Europe, but relying in the first on her strength, she strikes in full confidence of victory.

We declare the right of the people of Ireland to the ownership of Ireland and to the unfettered control of Irish destinies, to be sovereign and indefeasible. The long usurpation of that right by a foreign people and government has not extinguished that right, nor can it ever be extinguished except by the destruction of the Irish people. In every generation the Irish people have asserted their right to national freedom and sovereignty: six times during the past three hundred years they have asserted it in arms. Standing on that fundamental right and again asserting it in arms in the face of the world, we hereby proclaim the Irish Republic as a Sovereign Independent State, and we pledge our lives and the lives of our comrades-in-arms to the cause of its freedom, of its welfare and of its exaltation among the nations.

The Irish Republic is entitled to, and hereby claims, the allegiance of every Irishman and Irishwoman. The Republic guarantees religious and civil liberty, equal rights and equal opportunities to all its citizens, and declares its resolve to pursue the happiness and prosperity of the whole nation, and for all its parts, cherishing all the children of the nation equally, and oblivious of the differences, carefully fostered by an alien government, which have divided a minority from the majority in the past.

Until our arms have brought the opportune moment for the establishment of a permanent National Government, representative of the whole people of Ireland, and elected by the suffrages of all her men and women, the Provisional Government, hereby constituted, will administer the civil and military affairs of the Republic in trust for the people. We place the cause of the Irish Republic under the protection of the Most High God, Whose blessing we invoke upon our arms, and we pray that no one who serves that cause will dishonour it by cowardice, inhumanity or rapine. In this supreme hour the Irish nation must, by its valour and discipline, and by the readiness of its children to sacrifice themselves for the common good, prove itself worthy of the august destiny to which it is called."

Signed on Behalf of the Provisional Government
Thomas J. Clarke, Sean Mac Diarmada, Thomas MacDonagh,
P.H. Pearse, Eamonn Ceannt,
James Connolly, Joseph Plunkett

In the course of searching the Post Office upstairs, Collins and a detachment of volunteers, came across two barrels of porter which he immediately ordered to be smashed and poured out into drains to the astonishment of the Volunteers. Collins smiled and said: "It was drink that brought us down before, it won't happen this time!"

Throughout the week, as the British forces closed gradually and inexorably on Dublin, Collins thought through what was happening and when the shelling began to destroy one side of O'Connell Street, and set the G.P.O. on fire, he was convinced of the military folly of the Supreme Council. This was not the way! "We're fighting men who are vastly stronger on a battlefield than we are in direct onset; and they have the full military weight of the mighty Empire behind them. We have a few hundred volunteers, paying for their own rifles by weekly payment. There's a better way than this and the next time we will do it that better way." He was already thinking in terms of a "next time", A next time when he would not be just a Junior Officer.

Pearse was finally forced to surrender at the end of that red week and Collins was marched with the others to Richmond Barracks, to endure the ghoulish activities of the 'G' Division of the RIC as they prowled through the prisoners looking for wanted men, and picking men out for death. Collins and a few of his trusted friends spent this time intently gazing at these men, making notes or passing names and locations. When it was in his power to do so, he behaved with ruthless efficiency towards them. For a while, some of the leaders evaded recognition, but when they were identified they were eventually moved to Kilmainham Prison, and death.

Outside of Dublin, the rising was a military fiasco. Liam Mellowes strove valiantly to light the flames of rebellion in Galway, and managed to get a column of volunteers as far as Moyvore, in an attempt to reach the Shannon at Athlone, but were surrounded by troops and RIC, and local priests persuaded his men to slip away into the countryside, Mellowes escaped with great difficulty and finally got to America. In Ashbourne, in North County Dublin, a very significant action took place, which was keenly discussed later by Michael Collins. A small column of Volunteers attacked a much greater force of RIC, and after a fierce fight of some five hours, succeeded in forcing an enemy surrender, with considerable captures of material. The Volunteers were commanded by Thomas Ashe, a member of the Supreme Council of the Brotherhood, and his second-in-command was Richard Mulcahy, also a Brother, who was to cut a significant swathe in the future.

The Ashbourne battle resulted in the deaths of two volunteers and ten RIC; five volunteers and eighteen RIC were wounded, and this seminal guerrilla battle proved, in Michael Collin's questing mind, the great superiority of guerrilla actions over the standard military tactics of commandeering a building and waiting for the enemy to bring up artillery and machine guns, which was the abiding characteristic of the Easter Rising.

The Dublin Volunteers were marched in three lines the next day for transmission to English prisons, and a concentration camp in Wales – Frongoch. On the surrender march he saw the old, respected, venerable Tom Clarke being stripped and beaten and grossly maltreated on the order of Captain Lee Wilson of the RIC. Wilson was based in Wexford. Collins requested the Wexford men, whom he met later in Frongoch, to keep him constantly posted on Wilson's movements and two and a half years later, he paid Wilson back for his treatment of Tom Clarke – three bullets in his brain.

That was a long time in the future. This day, the defeated Volunteers marched towards the gangplank of the cattleship that was to take them to England and a very uncertain future.

The executions took place at intervals, like the solemn peals of a requiem bell. On 3 May, Patrick Pearse, Thomas Clarke and Thomas MacDonagh were shot: on 4 May, Joseph Plunkett, Ned Daly, Willie Pearse, Michael O'Hanrahan: on 8 May, Eamonn Ceannt, Michael Mallin of the Citizen Army, Con Colbert, the young paladin of the Fianna, and Sean Heuston were shot as was Thomas Kent of Cork on 9 May. On 12 May, James Connolly was carried out in a chair because of his shattered ankle, and shot, alongside Sean McDermott. Last of all, in lonely Pentonville Prison, Roger Casement was hanged.

The shootings had a severe effect on public opinion in Ireland. They went far towards rallying sympathy for the rebels. Then, with the treachery of the

Liberal Government in appointing most of the Orange rebels to high positions under the Crown and the persistent rumours of new legislation for conscription in Ireland, public opinion finally swung against the Parliamentary Party. As yet, this had not crystallised into support for the Republicans, but within a year it was to do so with decisive effect. One execution in particular, made a deep impression on the public mind.

On 3 May, Joseph Plunkett and Grace Gifford were married in a prison cell in Kilmainham. They were separated immediately afterwards, and the next morning he was taken out and done to death. With the exception of Casement, all were members of the IRB. All the signatories of the Proclamation of the Republic were executed.

FIVE

The University of Revolution

After the first week of confused activity and settling in, camp organisation began to emerge. Firstly, two football teams and an Irish class were started. One enthusiastic volunteer began preparations for amateur dramatics and this was the most popular of all. It was the custom of the clubs and associations when they met or performed to put up notices on the noticeboard outside one of the huts. It came as no surprise when less than a fortnight after the internees had been sent to Frongoch, there was a meeting in Hut B one morning at ten o'clock: A meeting of the committee of the Phoenix Literary and Debating Society. It would have seemed quite an informal meeting to anyone looking in from the outside and no one else was interested. The first football match was being played that morning and every internee who could possibly get there was present to cheer on his favourite team.

The first business of the meeting was to appoint a chairman and the respected Dublin solicitor, Henry Dixon, grey haired, proud, 69 years of age was the unanimous choice. He called the meeting to order. "Brothers, we all know why we are here. I call this the first meeting of the Frongoch Centre of the Irish Republican Brotherhood to order. I nominate Brother Michael Collins as secretary and I think that we are confident in electing this as a full centre. You are all true and tried brothers."

They determined to make use of the opportunity of having a thousand volunteers from all over Ireland in the camp. The Volunteers and all the voluntary organisations that were active in the country would be revived, and they would pick the best of the men who had proved themselves, to take leading positions in their organisations when they went back. They would also discuss the tactics of the coming fight. There were ten men present at that inaugural meeting of the Brotherhood, and they all were to play prominent parts in the history of the next ten years. Henry Dixon from Dublin had been on the Supreme Council of the Brotherhood for several years before, Dinny McCullough from Belfast also a member of the Council, young Michael Collins whom we met before, also present was Bill Mullins from Kerry, a strong-willed man, Michael Brennan from Clare, two more Cork men, Sean O'Muirthuile and Diarmuid O'Hegarty, a dark-visaged Tipperary man Frank Drohan, chirpy Neil Kerr from Liverpool and finally John McMahon from Dublin. These ten were to mould the future of the organisation of the Brotherhood and create the nucleus of a new Army from the volunteers out of

Ireland within the next three months.

They quickly went through a list of volunteers, deciding who should be approached and recruited, or in some cases, brought back into the Organisation. T.P. Daly, the socialist from the Post Office Union, Mike Staines, a Dublin man, Richard Mulcahy who was generally regarded as a good, sound recruit, Gearoid O'Suilleabhain, Sean Boylan from Dunboyne and another Daly, this time from Kerry were the first. Then, Tom Ennis, Joe O'Reilly, Padraig O'Maille, Simon Donnelly, Sean Hales, Sean T. O'Kelly, the Boland Brothers, Harry and Gerry. Their names were to be a roll of honour of the next five turbulent years.

"After all this." Henry said, "Our main purpose here is to act as a thinktank to evolve a strategy for the movement over the next few years. This internment will not last too long. We must decide what our strategy will be. We must not make the same fatal mistakes of divided authority, and of conventional warfare again."

Michael Collins said "I cannot conceal what I think. In future we will be different from in the past. We must be the leaven in the dough to make the bread rise, we must revive the volunteers because Ireland needs an Army. This must be the Army where we have control. There must never again be another McNeill, there must never again be another Redmond. But we must make it a different Army."

"We must make sure that we never stand and fight in a narrow ground where they can pull out all the artillery. We must strike them and run and retreat, and strike them again a few hours later somewhere else; and all over the country fight the war of the flea and the dog, the flea will bite and then jump, and the dog won't know where to scratch itself next. This is the difference between the splendid victory at Ashbourne, and the actual defeat in Dublin.

The new Army will be a People's Army – everyone in the country who believes in the cause will be a member – We will have a hundred thousand volunteers. But they will work away quietly for the most part. Every county will have several brigades, with battalions in every town, and a company in every townland. Each brigade must have a number of picked men like a Boer commando, who are fulltime guerrillas soldiers, with the mass of the Volunteers acting as eyes and ears and support in all possible ways, and cutting down trees and trenching roads to trap enemy trucks and columns for the active service commandos to move in for the kill.

But the fighting and the war is not the important thing, it is necessary to have the cutting edge of the armed struggle, but it is more important to break the people of their bovine belief in the Empire and the strength of the Empire, we have to take their minds from the Imperial structures, through which Ireland has been governed so long.

We have to destroy the Royal Irish Constabulary and establish our own police. The British Administration – we must blind and deafen all links of communication between them and the ordinary people of Ireland. We have to destroy the British courts and establish our own Irish courts, we have to take control of local authorities and pay our own taxes to them and our own rates. We must set up the whole administration of the State from the ground up, all as fast as we can and at whatever levels we can. And of course, the British will try and destroy us at every turn. But we must remember that it is not our task to take the best of our nation and put them up against British bullets with only a thin green uniform to protect them. What we must do is to build a new state inside the shell of the old one, until we can split the husk and emerge and when we have made the government of Ireland impossible for England, then we will have beaten England, despite all her navies and artillery."

The others could not forbear to cheer. His impassioned face, the determination with which he spoke and the content of those words carried them along. Their first meeting of the Frongoch Centre of the Irish Republican Brotherhood was to bear ample fruit.

From that day they worked with vigour. The leading Volunteers were approached and enrolled in the Brotherhood, and a schedule of military training began. They were determined to convert the bleak camp in North Wales into a university of Irish revolution, and in a few months they had succeeded.

In considering the tactics and lessons of the Rising, Collins was practical and clear-eyed. In writing to an old friend in West Cork, he analysed the tactics: "The actions of the leaders should not pass without comment. They have died nobly at the hands of the firing squads. So much I grant. But I do not think the Rising week was an appropriate time for the issue of memoranda couched in poetic phrases, nor of actions worked out in a similar fashion. Looking at it from the inside, it had the air of a Greek tragedy about it. These are sharp reflections. On the whole I think the Rising was bungled terribly, costing many a good life. It seemed at first to be well organised, but afterwards became subjected to panic decisions and a great lack of very essential organisation and co-operation."

A leading IRB lecturer in Frongoch was Richard Mulcahy, who was held in high esteem in the Camp, and was regarded as an excellent soldier and the military power behind the Battle of Ashbourne, where the RIC suffered heavy casualties, with the death of a County Inspector, a D.I. and many other ranks. Mulcahy outlined what was to be done whenever they were discharged from the camp. In the camp debates, he said, "Freedom will never come without a revolution, but, I fear the Irish people are too soft for that. To have a real revolution, you must have bloody, fierce minded men who don't care a scrap for death and bloodshed. A real revolution is not a job for children or for saints or scholars. In the course of a revolution, any man, woman or child, who is not with you, is against you. Put them up against a wall and shoot them. Shoot them and be dammed to them."

These sentiments of Mulcahy were the forerunner of the policies he was to use later during the Civil War, when he was Minister of Defence and Commander in Chief of the Army after Collins.

Each day as he walked through the camp, or played at games, or lounged in the mess Michael Collins was ceaselessly examining the faces of the men, remembering their names, measuring their words and assessing the strength and resolution of each. He was mentally building up the new Brotherhood, that would be the cutting edge of the next revolution, even then in gestation. In turn, his own influence and position among those fierce men was growing. Meanwhile, back in Ireland there had been a sea change in the attitude of the ordinary people of the land, not yet immediately discernible.

In the summer of 1916, the IRB members in Frongoch camp pursued their efforts to rebuild the organisation, to extend it's structure throughout every county that was represented, and to pick the key men of the Volunteers, by outlining the structure for the future. On the educational side, they expanded their activity with Irish classes and lessons in military technique, considerations and debates regarding the major economic and political questions that would face the new Ireland.

In this connection, one of the important things that the Brotherhood did, was to decide to establish a number of leading Irish companies, initially, on a small scale, but those which would have the opportunity of growth, and which would have the dual effect of providing employment and useful cover for members of the IRB, and of aiding the economic regeneration of the country. One of those of particular concern was the insurance industry. Collins was particularly anxious that there should be an Irish national insurance company formed, from his experience in Horner & Co., and the accountancy business both in London and Dublin. He was aware the enormous sums of money, constantly drained out of the national economy for British insurance companies, and one very important day they established the nucleus in Frongoch of a New Ireland Insurance Company. The leading figures in this were M.W. O'Reilly, Dennis McCullough and Michael Staines and to M.W. O'Reilly was given the task of piloting the infant company through it's early stages to become one of the important pillars of the new State, which he did with great efficiency.

A number of other projects of a similar nature were undertaken, all after careful consideration and exploration and with proper budgets laid down, development plans and people of chosen probity and knowledge and experience. Many of these projects, in various industrial fields, became pillars of the new State over the next twenty years.

Men, such as Alex McCabe, Lemass, Walton and many others, who later became important leaders in the business field received rudimentary training in business economies, budgets and accounts in the Hut classes in Frongoch and put that knowledge to good use later.

In July came the news of the Destruction of the Ulster Division in one bloody afternoon on the Somme. Nearly 40 times the casualties of Easter Week, the sombre news reinforced their determination to have another rising if the

English were foolish enough to attempt to enforce conscription on the Irish. There was no delight that a division of the British Army had been wiped out – only sorrow that so many Irishmen had thrown their lives away in an alien cause.

Back in Ireland, the mood of the people was changing very dramatically. In the beginning, there had been bewilderment over the suddenness of the Rising, disgust and cynicism over the bungling from a military point of view, with divided commands, and countermands. This was gradually replaced with sympathy, as day after day the announcements of the executions was given in terse and unfeeling military language. Then came the ominous news from Britain, as the question of partition was raised again, and the ever present threat of conscription. These combined to anger wide sections of the people, who were disgusted by the supine attitude of John Redmond and the Parliamentary Party. The Constitutional Movement was swiftly lampooned in song and verse throughout the country.

That summer, the British Government, particularly Asquith and Lloyd-George, were worried about the effect of Irish opinion upon the American election due that November. Numerous actions and activities of the IRB in American, with Clann na Gael, had increased tension and anti-British feeling as far as possible. They decided to make some attempt to defuse the anti-British sentiment in America and choose a particularly perfidious method of doing so.

Early in the summer, proposals were made to Carson and Redmond, whereby, the postponed Home Rule Act would be brought into operation immediately for Southern Ireland, but that six north-eastern Counties of Ulster would be excluded for an undetermined period, and this was to be, as far as the general public was concerned, for twelve months after the end of the War. This caused a considerable amount of confusion, though the general public, of course, and the Irish Parliamentary Party did not know that Lloyd-George had made a specific commitment to Carson of the British Government's support for Unionism, in a secret letter written from Whitehall, on 29 May 29 1916, as follows:

> "My Dear Carson,
>   I enclose Squires draft propositions [sic].
>   We must make it clear that at the end of the provisional period, Ulster does not, <u>whether she wills it or not,</u> merge with the rest of Ireland.
>
> Ever Sincerely,
> David Lloyd-George.
>
> P.S. Will you show this to Craig."

Then, when a furious Redmond finally realised how he had been tricked, he withdrew his assent and left the Parliament. However, the Home Rule Bill succeeded to a considerable extent in confusing the Irish in America and in blunting the opposition to any support for Britain in the War. In November of that year, Woodrow Wilson won the U.S. election, and Wilson's refusal to countenance Ireland's representation at the Versailles Peace Conference ensued that peace would only come to Ireland after five years of war.

At that time, General Maxwell, the butcher of Easter Week, had been recalled from Ireland. The British Government had decided in view of the increasing embarrassment in keeping the prisoners, they would end the Frongoch camp. The Government was in considerable difficulties, and Asquith resigned the Premiership. Lloyd-George became Prime Minister on 6 December. Sir Edward Carson retained his post as First Lord of the Admiralty and Bonar Law, the Conservative and Unionist Leader, became Chancellor of the Exchequer and Leader of the House of Commons. A few days before Christmas, the Chief Secretary for Ireland declared that the time had come that the risk of liberating the internees would be less that the risk which might follow by detaining them any longer.

On the following day, the prisoners were released from Frongoch, and to their amazement, when they arrived in Westland Row, they were greeted with bonfires and torchlight processions, parades through the streets with thousands of cheering citizens; the same people who only eight months before had greeted them with disdain as they marched into captivity. It was obvious that change had commenced. As Collins and the others celebrated, they were determined that the holiday period would be short – there was a rich harvest to be gathered. The IRB were determined that they would reap that harvest.

The biggest single factor in the change was the looming threat of conscription. By the end of 1916, the western powers were in dire straits in Flanders and in France. Both Britain and France had been drained of manpower by the years of indeterminate trench warfare. Carson was continuously demanding that conscription should be applied in Ireland. It appeared as if the Government was about to give way. This proved decisive in bringing large sections of the Irish population to supporting the rebels. The horror of being forcibly taken and thrust into the killing fields of France, where two out of every three would die, loomed over every Irish youth. Even the Catholic bishops were forced to change their tune and give tacit support to the wave of anti-conscription feeling.

Included in the cheering crowds in the streets were the frequent appearances of tricolours. There was little indication of the change that had taken place on the ground, in people's hearts. In 1917, this change was to become visible in the drumroll of by-elections, which the IRB had decided would be suitable battlegrounds to fight. The new task before the Brotherhood was, firstly, to consolidate and extend their own organisation, tighten up the administration, to take the steps to provide themselves with an Army, to revive the Volunteer structure and this time to make certain that there were no divided councils. The Army was to be totally responsive to the desires and instructions of the Brotherhood on all major questions. They set out to provide themselves with the Army by summoning a secret convention to rebuild the Volunteers.

SIX

The Conventions

The returned prisoners did not celebrate for long: from the second week of January 1917, they had begun to plan the next round. The intention was to knit together the disparate strands of the organisation and develop a new Brotherhood Centre in every county. In the middle of January, Count Plunkett, father of Joseph Plunkett of the IRB, who was executed at Easter 1916, was expelled from the Royal Dublin Society because of his family's connections with the Rising, although he had given long and remarkable service to the agricultural and co-operative movement in Roscommon. The RDS was an ultra-loyal, mainly Anglo-Irish Society, ostensibly founded to encourage agriculture and commerce.

There was a by-election pending in Roscommon. Harry Boland, the indefatigable organiser and friend of Collins was the first choice amongst the IRB activists in the county. But Boland was a rare combination of idealism and intelligence. Clearly, Count Plunkett would be a more popular candidate with the electorate, and although Harry could easily have obtained a nomination, and the glory of winning the first seat for the Republic, he put the temptation behind him and organised the nomination, and the election, for Plunkett. The campaign was intended to deliver a knockout punch to the Irish Parliamentary Party, and to illustrate what the people thought of the Royal Dublin Society. Collins travelled to Roscommon and, on joining forces with the redoubtable Boland, campaigned vigorously. Plunkett stood on the issue of "abstention" and endorsement of the Republic. Collins wrote his election address, containing such phrases as; "No Irish MP should take his seat in anything but an Irish Parliament. Because he will not associate with Irishmen who cheered when his son was put up against a wall and shot for loving Ireland .... The Royal Dublin Society decided to expel him, and tell you that he is not the man you want? NO! There are Irishmen in Roscommon YET!" The result of the election was a tremendous victory for Plunkett and, by extension, for the IRB. It was a disaster for the Irish Parliamentary Party.

Collins was appointed as fulltime Secretary of the National Aid Association and Volunteers Dependants Fund. The appointment was organised by the Provisional Council of the IRB which had been urgently reformed in Dublin at the end of August, under cover of the Oireachtas of the Gaelic League. The new Council included men like Diarmuid O'Hegarty and Thomas Ashe.

Later, following the release of the convicted prisoners in mid-June in 1917, the IRB appointed a new Supreme Council and proceeded to draft a new constitution. For the first time, Michael Collins became a member of the Supreme Council. Collins and Ashe along with Dermot Lynch and Con Collins drafted the new and improved Constitution. Specific provision was made for the inclusion of a military council.

There was an urgent need to adopt the new Constitution of the IRB and to consider the opportunities inherent in the new national situation. Accordingly there was a full convention that spring, this time entirely secret, and this time, of the Brotherhood. The veteran President of the Supreme Council, Joe McGarry, resigned and was replaced by Thomas Ashe, the hero of Ashbourne. Michael Collins became General Secretary, with Liam O'Muirthuile as Treasurer. These three comprised the working executive of the Brotherhood, the dynamo of the whole insurrectionary movement. As Secretary of the IRB, Michael Collins organised both conventions and all country members of the Brotherhood were requested to meet him before attending the conventions, of the re-organised Volunteers and of the new political alliance of Republicans that were to adopt the name of Sinn Féin, roughly translated as "Ourselves Alone".

The next month, there was the first important convention to decide the political course of the next phase of the struggle, representing all the disparate strands of the movement for national regeneration. The convention was held in the Mansion House, municipal centre of Dublin. The IRB were not able to stage-manage the entire convention, but they were able, by quick reactions, to guide it away from the dangerous and beguiling channels of moderation.

Count Plunkett first proposed to start a new political movement, scrapping all existing groups, including the tiny Sinn Féin, with himself as president. Griffiths did not agree. The IRB honest brokers succeeded in getting approval for the establishment of a loose alliance of national groupings, under the banner of Sinn Féin, based firmly on abstention from Westminster and the summoning of a new All-Ireland National Parliament in Dublin – Dáil Éireann. With much swallowing of pride from Griffiths and Plunkett, Eamon De Valera, the last Commandant to surrender on Easter Week, was unanimously selected to head the new organisation. Michael Collins and Harry Boland were elected to the executive. There was little attempt to evolve practical political programmes in detail. Sinn Féin was a populist movement, short on theory and long on practical organisation, imbued with the ethos of the Brotherhood.

At this stage a sharp difference of opinion arose within Sinn Féin, between Ashe and Collins, as leaders of the IRB, and De Valera and Brugha, both former Brothers. De Valera and Brugha urged that the IRB had outlived its usefulness, and as a secret society, came under the condemnation of the Catholic Hierarchy. Ashe settled the argument with a trenchant statement:

"Have we yet reached the state of power when we can afford to cast aside a proven ideal for a barely proven one? Are we so great that we can afford a quarrel amongst ourselves oblivious to the common enemy? Men and movements should be as nothing in this time of great test: Country – our country of Ireland should be the main thought."

The IRB compromised a little and adopted a low profile for a while, but worked to ensure domination of the GHQ staff of the Volunteers, and strong representation on the executive of the regenerated Sinn Féin, which was shaping as a broadly based populist party with little political ideology. It's first test was a by-election in Longford, the following month. The IRB/Sinn Féin candidate was a republican prisoner in Lewes Prison named J.J. McGuinness.

This election was to assume great significance in the life of Michael Collins and Harry Boland. They both practically ran McGuinness's election and they were regarded as a superb election team. During the campaign they stayed often in a hotel called the Greville Arms, in Granard, owned by a family called Kiernan, three sisters and a brother. One of the girls, Kitty Kiernan, was a vivacious, attractive young woman of great charm, and many admirers. Both Collins and Boland fell in love with her, during the hectic campaign, and their three lives intertwined for the next five years. Kitty played the two men on a string, and both were infatuated with her. Both asked her to marry them but she dallied, not wishing to make a definite decision. Despite this rivalry, Harry and Michael remained good friends and faithful collaborators. Thomas Ashe, the third most assiduous IRB election worker, and who had been Commandant at the battle of Ashbourne during Easter Week, was courting another Kiernan sister, Maud.

The Longford election was bitterly fought and the IRB candidate won by a whisker, 37 votes. The Brotherhood was satisfied with another blow at the Constitutional movement, and proceeded to the next step, a nationwide campaign for Prisoners-of-War status for sentenced Republican prisoners. There were scores of agitational meetings all over the country. One of these meetings, which were often the scene of conflict between Volunteers and the Police, led to the death of a Detective-Inspector of the Royal Irish Constabulary who was struck on the head with a hurley stick during a fracas. The Government immediately banned the carrying of hurley sticks in public places.

From the next weekend, almost every teenager and many thousands of sedentary citizens who had never played hurling in their lives, and never intended to, paraded out for their Sunday walks with hurleys over their shoulders. The Government wisely turned a blind eye.

Another significant by-election loomed up, in County Clare. The professor of mathematics, Eamon De Valera, last Commandant to survive Easter Week, and President of Sinn Féin, was chosen as candidate. After a whirlwind campaign, De Valera won the election by 5,000 votes to 2,000 for the Parliamentary Party candidate.

The election marked the emergence of De Valera as a national leader, and the eclipse of the Constitutional Party. During the campaign, the Volunteers, wearing green uniforms, acted as stewards and guardians at De Valera's meetings and contributed greatly to the enthusiasm of the people, by directing and marshalling the crowds. The Government and the RIC were powerless to interfere.

A month later, W.T. Cosgrave, just released after being sentenced to "life imprisonment", was elected in another by-election, this time in County Kilkenny. The Parliamentary Party's horror increased when their most popular MP, Laurence Ginnell, who had been a staunch supporter of the men in Frongoch and other prisoners, announced that he was resigning from the Parliamentary Party, withdrawing from Parliament in Westminster, and joining Sinn Féin. The Republican juggernaut was unstoppable, and the extinction of Redmond's Party was widely predicted.

The twin dynamos, Michael Collins and Harry Boland, carefully nurtured and directed the growth of Sinn Féin during this crucial year. Collins was more in the background – he had other fish to fry – but Boland emerged more and more as the guiding political spirit and managing director of the political side of the movement. De Valera, as President, was more concerned with cerebral politics and policy manifestos, whilst Boland tightened the nuts and bolts of the organisation, and ensured that the key men in each county were reliable Brothers. Boland never sought personal publicity and his work was mostly in the background. He has been largely ignored but he was a man of great bravery and he possessed a superb political brain. His contribution to the Irish Revolution was immense, his sacrifice total.

Collins was laying the groundwork for the formal reviving and restructuring of the Volunteers as the national army, and the Convention to do this met on 26 October. It was a "People's Army" with the political and military side of the movement co-ordinated and integrated. The IRB contained most of the more intelligent, active and motivated officers, and almost all of the Battalions and Brigade Staff had IRB Commandants and Adjutants. Eamon De Valera was appointed as President, uniting in a single person the overall political and military leadership. An executive was elected, of which Collins was a member and this executive appointed the GHQ staff, many of whom were also Sinn Féin activists, and almost all were of the IRB. There was clearly going to be no more divided councils – no more McNeills. It was indeed a "People's Army", fully integrated and synonymous with the revolutionary movement, Sinn Féin.

Donning another of his hats, Collins became Director of Organisation, on GHQ staff, an amorphous post which could mean as much as the energy and initiative of its occupant – and Collins had plenty of both.

There was a tiny cloud on the horizon, which could and did grow as the years passed. The COIR, the President or Head Centre of the Brotherhood, was recognised by the Brothers as the virtual President of the Irish Republic. Yet, De Valera was President of Sinn Féin and of the Army of the Republic, in the eyes of the people, whatever the Brotherhood and the chief officers of the

Army might think. This dichotomy was to grow and fester, and after Collins became Head Centre, was to delineate the divisions of the future Civil War.

But all this was in the future, and men are sometimes blessed that they do not foresee what is to come. As 1917 drew to a close, the Brotherhood was well contented. They were back in business, only eighteen months after the bloodbath of Easter Week; they controlled a fast growing national political movement of Resurgence; and they had a national army again, better organised that ever before. Before them loomed the incessant fight for political status in the prisons: the battleground of other by-elections, and preparations for the "Khaki" election of 1918.

The struggle for political status, or prisoner-of-war status occupied a great deal of attention. Many officers had been arrested, and there was a continual series of arrests under the DORA, the Defense of the Realm Act. Collins himself had been arrested in Sligo and skipped bail and the Republican prisoners invariably refused to do any prison work, to wear a prison uniform, or accept the criminal regime that the British attempted to impose, and wherever possible, to control and force them to mix with ordinary criminals. This was the key factor in every prison both in Britain and in Ireland where there were Republican prisoners, and the prison population was steadily growing. One of the most celebrated cases was that of Thomas Ashe, a leading member of the Volunteers, of Sinn Féin and President of the Council of the Brotherhood. Having been arrested for a seditious speech, he refused to wear prison clothes and encouraged everyone else in the prison to go on hunger strike. After four days, the prison governor attempted to forcibly feed the prisoners, which is normally a cruel but reasonably safe operation. However, in the case of Thomas Ashe, the doctor or the warders performing the operation of feeding each prisoner with soup through a tube, used a considerable amount of force, much more than what was necessary, and severely damaged Ashe's lungs and stomach, as a result of which, he went into a coma. He died the next day.

His funeral was an immense display of national feeling. The British Army and the RIC wisely stayed away from the entire proceedings, which were stewarded by Volunteers in uniform and attended by a 100,000 people. The oration was given at the grave by Michael Collins in the uniform of a Staff Officer. A very short speech was made immediately after the firing of a volley of salute over the grave of Thomas Ashe. Collins concluded his speech with a pungent phrase, "That volley which you have just heard is the most fitting thing to say over the grave of a Fenian". The funeral of Thomas Ashe helped enormously to consolidate the spirit of the Volunteers and arouse the enthusiasm of Sinn Féin, as had the previous funeral of O'Donovan Rossa, and helped to lay the groundwork of the New Volunteer Army.

Stung by the enormous outpouring of national spirit, the Government finally decided to act to crush the growing menace. They concocted a scheme called the "German Plot" in which they hoped to allege successfully that many of the leaders of Sinn Féin and the Volunteer movement were in negotiation with Germany and laying plans for a German invasion of Ireland. There was not a scintilla of truth in this allegation but the Government used this as an excuse for widespread imprisonment and internment. Collins, however, had begun to cultivate some of the detectives in Dublin Castle whom he later found of enormous value in the struggle, and one of them, Kavanagh, came early into possession of some information regarding the proposed Government swoop. He quickly got the information to Collins, a day and a half before the round-up was to take place. Collins immediately informed the Executive of Sinn Féin and of the Volunteers of what was planned. Somewhat to his surprise, many of the leading activists, both in Sinn Féin and the Volunteers, whose names were on the list declined to take evasive action from a variety of motives, and went about their normal business and slept in their normal beds. Of course, they were arrested, and for the next two or three months they were fairly safe from all tumult. Amongst those arrested were De Valera and Griffiths. The IRB were ordered to "go on the run" and they all avoided arrest. Collins and Boland and their closest associates avoided arrest quite simply. Collins slept in the bed of a man who had been arrested an hour before, on the theory that they would not return.

One of the unforeseen consequences of the removal of the leaders of the "German Plot", was that those they left behind, for a considerable time had total control of the organisation, both of Sinn Féin and of the rapidly growing Volunteers. Collins and Boland made full use this golden opportunity. Sinn Féin was preparing to fight the "Khaki" election, the one that would follow the end of the War, and Collins and Boland, brilliantly, laid the groundwork for the enormous victory during that election. They very carefully went through the lists of active members, particularly, ensuring that those who would be nominated as candidates for the election were of strong moral fibre, and making sure, in Boland's mordant phrase, "that the hideous fangs of moderation do not arise".

Most of the candidates that they picked to be deputies in the Dail were experienced men who had been well tried, who had been in prisons, either in Frongoch or elsewhere, or had fought in 1916. They did their best to exclude people who were, in their opinion, unreliable, even people like Darrel Figgis who had been an old IRB man, but who was regarded by Collins as a windbag, despite his close connections with Griffiths and his leading position in Sinn Féin. This caused considerable tension between Collins and Griffiths. Despite some maudlin sentiments long after both men were dead, Griffiths never entirely trusted Collins after this incident, and he still hankered after the obsolete concept of a "dual monarchy", a ghost which returned to haunt Sinn Féin in the Treaty negotiations.

But for Collins, the day's victory was the important thing and he made sure that when the Dáil met they would have a solid Republican cadre. He did not trust any of the old "King's Lords and Commons" men who had been with Griffiths since 1905 and he was determined that the fighting officers of the field who would have to bear the brunt of the battle, would be those, who would decide in the final analysis, the terms upon which the War would end, and indeed, when it would end.

Lloyd-George made two major mistakes in 1918. The first was in April when he introduced a bill to extend conscription to Ireland, which immediately led to the final withdrawal of the Irish Parliamentary Party from Westminster, and the total alienation of a great majority of men and women in the country. They naturally showed their sympathies towards the Volunteers and Sinn Féin, and most of the men who would have been caught in the conscription net, spurned them to join the Volunteers instead.

The threat of conscription, more than the emotional feeling over the executions of the 1916 men, was the decisive factor that swung the country to Sinn Féin. The second major mistake, possibly the greater, was that for an important period of several months, they had arranged that all the leaders of Sinn Féin, all the public leaders, who also happened to be the most moderate, be arrested. And in doing so they left, still at large, the redoubtable pair of Michael Collins and Harry Boland, and quickly, these two restless revolutionaries divided up the national movement between them. Boland was to rigorously go through the Sinn Féin Party, and prepare it for the inevitable election that was coming, which would be the greatest and probably the final test of strength between Sinn Féin and the Parliamentary Party. Collins concentrated on preparing the Army for the fight that he was quite determined would commence immediately after the election and the summoning of Dáil Éireann. The fertile ground was laid before them. They had virtually no political or military rivals. All the moderates who would have prevented them from getting an iron grip on both the Army and the political movement were in prison at the time. The two happy conspirators worked all the hours that God gave. For a brief period the political and military wings of the Irish Revolution were in the capable hands of two competent, energetic and mutually trusting leaders. In those crucial months, the pattern of events over the next four thunderous years was woven and it was woven to Michael Collins's design.

SEVEN

Victory

The Armistice in the bloody War in Europe came on the 11 November, and next month, on the 14 December, was the long awaited General Election. Collins planned to strike a deadly blow at the enemy. He and Boland had prepared the ground well. The majority of the Sinn Féin candidates were, in fact, in prisons in England, and the old slogan, "Put them in, to get them out" was used to great effect. Throughout the country, there was the most extraordinary upsurge of national feeling and the result provided a stunning upset, almost without parallel in democratic elections anywhere. Of 105 seats, Sinn Féin won 73. Redmond's Parliamentary Party were reduced to six and even that was mostly because of a trick that had been played on Collins and Boland by Sir James McMahon and the Castle supported by Cardinal Logue, under the guise of joint Catholic-Irish Party Candidates, and the Unionists had 26. The Unionist and the six Irish Party\"Catholic Candidates" attended the Commons at Westminster. It was a total and absolute repudiation of the Parliamentary Party and the British connection. Sinn Féin had conveyed quite clearly its attitude. Of the 73 elected, the majority were IRB members. Most of the major prisoners, including Griffiths and De Valera, had also been elected. The celebrations were long. Collins and Boland, at first, could hardly believe it themselves, their success was so total.

Meanwhile the new British Cabinet met. Lloyd-George was again Prime Minister, Walter Long, First Lord of the Admiralty, Winston Churchill, Secretary of State for War, Galloper Smith, now Lord Birkenhead, was Lord Chancellor and Bonar Law was Leader of the House of Commons. The Cabinet appointed Ian McPherson as Chief Secretary for Ireland and left Lord French in the position of Lord Lieutenant. These were the antagonists of the Brotherhood; the struggle was to be bitter.

On the diplomatic front, the Dáil and the new Executive had been busy. Even before the Dáil met, they had appointed the deputation to proceed to London and to interview President Woodrow Wilson on his way through to the Peace Conference in Paris, to seek recognition and a place for the Irish at the Conference table. They also appointed Sean T. O'Kelly as Irish Minister in France and Dr. Pat McCartan as Minister in the United States of America. Both were staunch members of the Brotherhood. McCartan was one of the members of the Supreme Council, and an old Tyrone Republican. The delegation appointed to meet Wilson included Collins, Sean T. O'Kelly, Bob

Barton and Gavan Duffy, with O'Kelly as head of the delegation. They promptly travelled to London where they were lionised by various Irish groups and friends of Ireland, and were briefly the target of the British and the international press.

In London, Collins and Sean T. O'Kelly were guests at the comfortable Kensington home of Crompton and Moya Llewellyn-Davis, and early in their stay, the Davis' hosted a glittering London society dinner for the Irish delegation. Amongst the guests were Sir James Barrie, author of *Peter Pan* and uncle of Crompton, who was a relative of Churchill and had been a prominent officer in the British Secret Service during the War. Another guest was a tall officer in the Secret Service whom we have met before. He was introduced to Collins and they shook hands pressing their thumbs together in an odd little gesture which no one noticed. The tall officer was Major John Charteris.

The talk at that dinner was at a glittering level. Barrie who was a noted British intellectual, became quite entranced in conversation with Collins. Sean T. was more withdrawn and slightly ill at ease in the presence of people who he subconsciously regarded as the enemy. But Collins was on familiar ground. Lady Moya smiled and sparkled, occasionally looking at him approvingly and with the odd amorous glance. Crompton smiled indulgently and waved his cigar in the air to illuminate his points. John Charteris mentioned his move to Ireland in charge of security and the munitions industry in the first few years of the War and that he had a particular responsibility for ICI Eley Kynoch munitions factory in Arklow.

As far as the press and the British Government knew generally, the Irish delegation were on their way to Paris. However, it was almost certain that at the dinner at the Llewellyn-Davis', in the course of conversation, it would emerge they had hoped to meet President Woodrow Wilson in London. Unfortunately, Barrie, who was the senior British Secret Service agent present, would have felt it his duty to discuss this matter, and the next day, sufficient pressure was put upon Wilson through diplomatic circles, that the American Government felt that is was quite impossible due to time pressure, to meet the Irish delegation. Consequently, Sean T. O'Kelly went to Paris on his own and the rest of the delegation returned to Ireland. Sean T. set in motion the procedure to acquire an official embassy office there which would be headquarters of the Irish movement and administration in France. He looked around, and had recommended a very good person who spoke perfect English, French and Italian. She was an Italian called Annie Vivanti, who happened to be married to John Charteris, and became O'Kelly's secretary and a very useful member of the Embassy staff.

The next day Collins met John Charteris, and after some preliminary sparring, swore him into the Brotherhood. He was to be worth his weight in gold as a double agent. This tangible result of the visit of the delegation to London was that on the morning after the dinner in Kensington, Collins returned for coffee to have a private meeting with his old friend. The blood brothers gave each other a warm welcome and brought each other up to date on their respective careers. Charteris had been for a period in charge of security at munitions factories and had spent some time in the middle east on intelligence duties with MI6 during which time he met some exotic characters including T.E. Lawrence, who was then indulging his penchant for guerrilla warfare and with whom he became friendly. He looked at Collins with a quizzical eye, knowing perfectly well that in the business in which both men were engaged and the crux of events of the time there would be little point in social visits. He had made it quite clear that his sympathies were with the Republicans since the suppression of the Easter Rising, and without being obvious, he practically invited an offer from Collins.

"Do you wish to help the movement ?"

Charteris looked out the window for a moment and after a long pause, said:

"I will do what I can – You know my position."

Collins said "For your own security you would have to be sworn into the Brotherhood. Anything might happen to me and there must be at least one other Brother, who can vouch for you. There will be only one other who will know your identity, whom you can approach if I am removed from the scene. That would be Florrie O'Donoghue, the Head Centre in Cork who is as silent as the tomb."

Charteris said "There is a chance that neither of us might survive. How many people would need to know?"

Collins laughed and said "Only me but I will leave a message with this very sound man in Cork and he will contact you if anything happens to me through Moya and you can contact him through her. You can also contact me anytime through Moya."

Charteris thought deeply for a moment. "For disinformation I must always be referred to as "Lieutenant G" If they find any paper or report, that will send them up a false trail".

Charteris reached his hand out Collins took it and they pressed together the little scars on their thumbs and each repeated "Your enemies will be mine. I will never take up arms against you even though our own kin shall be at war". Collins briefly administered the Oath of the Brotherhood which he had received himself ten tumultuous years before in Islington.

It appears that the IRB and Collins had tremendous efficiency and capability in penetrating British intelligence at a comparatively low level, the security level in Ireland in regards to police, spies, touts and so forth and the movement of troops, but they had no contact whatsoever with the British political establishment. They seemed to have been, all during the progress of the Anglo-Irish War, completely unaware of the main currents of thought within the British Cabinet and within the British general establishment, so that while militarily they seemed to have little difficulty to fighting the British to a standstill and building up a separate administration, they never really grasped the problem that they had to overcome, in the diplomatic and political intelligence field – the speciality of the British establishment. John Charteris was the highest-level operative in Collin's stable and there were hugh areas of political and diplomatic activity on the British side, on which he could only hazard a guess.

On the other hand, for the British, with centuries of experience, just on that task, behind them, Ireland was an open book; all its political thought, all the internal discussions, divisions, and possibilities, in its leadership, in the Dáil and in Sinn Féin were visible and known to the British Cabinet from the very beginning. It could have been predicted that almost certainly the Irish would win the War, and almost certainly, they would lose the Peace.

On 21 January 1919, the first Dáil met for the first time in the Mansion House in Dublin. The President of the Assembly was Cathal Brugha, a hero of the Rising. Collins, Boland and others were away in England on urgent business – attempting to rescue De Valera from Lincoln Prison. Collins was also engaged on a diplomatic mission for the infant Republic, seeking recognition from the U.S. president, Woodrow Wilson.

The eyes of the World, for that day, focused upon Dublin, where the rebel Parliament was meeting. Huge crowds besieged the Mansion House, and the entire public rose and watched with great excitement when a somewhat self-conscious 27 elected deputies walked into the Round Room and took their place. The roll call was made and for most of the names, the clerk of the Dáil answered "Faoi glas ag Sasan" (Imprisoned in England). The provisional Constitution of Dail Eireann was read, providing for a President with a ministry of four and then the Declaration of Independence was read. The Assembly had solemnly constituted themselves as a Parliament and choose its elected delegates to present Ireland's case to the Peace Conference meeting in Paris. Michael Collins was one of the delegates chosen, with Sean T. O'Kelly as Head. O'Kelly became the second President of a free nation 25 years later.

The first Dáil that day also adopted the "Democratic Programme" a very progressive Manifesto of social justice, and in the Declaration of Independence firmly locked the door on any compromise of a unitary Republic.

The next day, Collins and Boland read the accounts in the newspapers, while busily engaged in attempting to spring De Valera from Lincoln Jail. They also read inflammatory paragraphs detailing how a gang of Irish murderers had attacked the RIC in Tipperary in attempting to steal some gelignite and killed two of the policemen. The first shots had been fired by Dan Breen and Sean Tracey. Collins was a bit annoyed, he liked things tidy and he had not given permission for this operation. However, there was more urgent business to be done. After a number of farcical adventures, with keys which broke when turned, they finally succeeded, and De Valera and two companions made their way in through the grounds to the side gate to which they had already been presented with the proper key. Eventually, De Valera was freed.

Within a day or two, the British were so annoyed by the apparently easy release of De Valera that they decided to pretend that they knew all about it, and had connived at it and promptly released all the other elected deputies. On 22 March, a statement was sent by Harry Boland, announcing that De Valera would be received with national rejoicing and a procession would be made with a meeting from the gates of the City, to the Mansion House, where he would deliver a message to the Irish people. This had not been sanctioned by the Executive or by De Valera or Griffiths and caused a good deal of annoyance within the organisation. It also caused the first serious and formal row between Griffiths and Collins, and eventually when De Valera sided with Griffiths, Collins had to retract and Boland cancelled the proposed meeting. It seems clear that the two master agitators had intended a monstrous and deliberate provocation to the Castle. If they had misread the temper of the authorities there might easily have been a bloody massacre at the Mansion House. It was a political defeat and a warning to the IRB that they could not take everyone else for granted.

Collins had also been involved in the rescue of another Republican deputy, Bob Barton, a protestant landowner in County Wicklow and a former senior officer in the British Army, who had come over to the Republican cause after 1916. The week after, Dáil Eireann met for the second time, and this time did more serious business, De Valera was formally elected "Priomh Aire", Prime Minister of the Dail Ministry and his Cabinet was announced. Michael Collins became Minister of Finance, which in effect was number two man in the Government. Others in the Cabinet were Griffiths, Austin Stack, Cathal Brugha, William Cosgrave, and Robert Barton. Other members of the Republican Government, outside the Cabinet, included Eoin MacNeill, George Plunkett and the Countess Markievitz. She was the first woman Government minister in the World.

The very next day began the immense task of constructing the rebel administration under the nose of and against the enormous opposition of the existing Government, but as the first step, a subterranean civil service had to be built up, and the first most important step was the creation of a major public loan organised by Michael Collins. The money was to be collected in Ireland and America and throughout other friendly countries.

The second most important appointment of the Dail Government was that of Cathal Brugha as Minister of Defence. As a Minister, Brugha was not a success. He continued with his full time business of candle-making and he informed the Cabinet that he would not be drawing his Dáil or Cabinet salary, but in fact, would be donating it to the Chief of Staff for the purposes of the Army. This was a sort of gesture that meant that he did not treat his responsibilities seriously enough to become the actual administrator of the Department of Defence.

However, nature and revolutions have a horror of vacuums, and if Brugha didn't operate in the Department of Defence, the administration of the Department quickly came under the pervasive grip of Michael Collins who was

Director of Organisation, and also Director of Intelligence, and of Richard Mulcahy, who was Chief of Staff of the rebel Army. A certain continuous discord in the key department arose from the fact that Brugha, the Minister of Defence, was paranoid about the IRB, to which all his senior officers belonged. In practice, the Army came to almost ignore the Minister, as far as the actual daily administration was concerned, and got on with the job of running the War.

From mid 1917 to mid 1919, Collins, in fact, was Adjutant General as well, being replaced later by Gearoid O'Suilleabhain. At this stage, he was the key person organising the IRB Volunteer movement, and the development and prosecution of the Anglo-Irish War.

An important channel for IRB philosophy within the new Volunteer Army, was *An t-Oglac,* a four page Volunteer sheet, which was directed and produced by Collins, and to which he contributed notes on the Organisation. *An t-Oglac* became the guide book and primer for new theories on guerrilla warfare.

In the spring of 1919, Collins ceded the posts of the Adjutant General and Director of Organisation of the Volunteers to Gearoid O'Suilleabhain and Diarmuid O'Hegarty. He threw himself with greater initiative into his new role as Director of Intelligence, building up the network of spies and informers, and intelligence operators highly placed in the British machine, which in the end nullified all the efforts of Dublin Castle. By the middle of 1919, Collins had become President of the Supreme Council of the IRB, a post which he held for the rest of his life.

He was also "President of the Irish Republic" in the eyes of the IRB, but an invisible President known only to the Brothers. De Valera was Prime Minister of the Dáil, but was also President of Sinn Féin and of the Irish Volunteers (IRA) both highly visible posts.

Now began the most important part of Michael Collins's life, the part which had the most influence on history, and that which was the foundation of the legend of Collins. He had given a great deal of thought to past risings and conspiracies in Ireland and had come to the conclusion that the reason why almost all of them had failed was because of penetration by agents of the Castle into the revolutionary movement. Almost all the rebellions against the Crown had been aborted, particularly 1798, by the enormous numbers of spies and informers that the British had throughout the country. The same was true of the beginnings of the Fenian movement. Even Collins did not know then to what extent this litter of spies had actually been successful, and how enduring it was.

He was well aware that there could be no successful Irish revolution, as long as the eyes and ears of the Castle, the Royal Irish Constabulary, and the even greater network of sympathetic agents, mainly through loyalist Anglo-Saxon landowners, retired officers, various pensioners and hangers-on of the Empire, continued to provide continuous information on all aspects of Irish life. He resolved that this would be changed. His resolution meant that he would break the connection between the informers and the Castle. He would encourage all those who felt like informing, to reflect upon the dangers of such, and to adopt an attitude of scrupulous neutrality towards the battle that was about to commence, or else to die.

It was essential for him that he would have his own parallel intelligence organisation, one which would, even on a smaller scale, find out as much as possible about the military dispositions, the police intelligence and all the plans of the enemy and also that he would have at his hand, a punitive organisation, performing the necessary surgery.

From the beginning, luck was with Collins and four extremely well-placed and intelligent detectives in the upper echelons of the G-Division of Dublin Castle, very quickly revealed themselves to him as sympathetic to the Irish cause. The first of these was Joe Kavanagh, who had made various attempts to get in touch with the leaders of the movement, and eventually managed to contact Collins. He was extremely highly placed and provided much, extraordinarily useful information, including the warning, through Collins to the leaders, of the British intention to swoop and arrest them all. Kavanagh, unfortunately died of ill-health towards the end of 1920.

By then, there had been three others who had replaced him. One was Eamonn Broy, who became known as the famous Colonel Ned Broy, after whom the Broy Harriers were called. Broy was a dire, rugged, determined man, trusted totally by the Castle, and in a position to provide tremendous information.

On one occasion, Broy brought Collins into the Detective Headquarters in Brunswick Street. The other detectives present and the guards in the Castle assumed because of Collins's sturdy build and looks and because of the company he was in, that he also was a detective. Collins and Broy spent the entire night going through various files that related to operations all over the country. Collins was greatly taken to find his own file, in which he was described as coming from a "brainy" West Cork family. He made copious notes over a period of several hours and by the time he went out of the Castle the next morning, he had within his pockets, the secrets of almost the entire structure of active current British spies in Ireland. It was invaluable information. It was also death warrants for the men concerned.

Collins walked out the next morning and went down to a meeting in the Dáil, in the Mansion House. He gave no hint of the extraordinary night that he had spent in the innermost citadel of the enemy. He deliberately made a sensational entrance having dressed in full staff officer's uniform, complete with red tabs, and the foreign press went into paroxysms of delight. Here was the "Most Wanted Man" appearing in public in the rebel uniform. He was the only officer so dressed and as the photographers jostled each other, the Minister of Defence scowled sourly. This meeting was raided by the military, in a vain search for him, but Collins simply walked out through a side door and waited in an adjoining building until the troops had left, then returned to the business of the meeting. His legend lost nothing in the telling.

The second leg of Collins's organisation for the intelligence division was a team of extremely competent officers. Tom Cullen, who had been the Captain of the Wicklow Volunteers, Frank Thornton from the Dublin ASU, and Liam Tobin and Joe Dolan. These four comprised Collins's full time Intelligence Staff and they were his direct link to the Squad. Following the momentous night that he spent in Brunswick Street Detective Division, he had divided up the notes in regard to Dublin spies amongst these four, and they made their arrangements accordingly. A key member of the staff was Joe O'Reilly who had been with him in Frongoch, and his devotion to "The Big Fellow", as Collins was nicknamed was legendary.

In addition to Collins's direct plans to deal with the intelligence sources of G-Division, he also, by virtue of having got all their addresses, arranged that formidable looking members of the Dublin Brigade and the ASU would call on them at their homes and stress to them how inadvisable it would be to if they were too enthusiastic in their service for the Crown; that there was a change coming, and if they wanted to be alive in the new situation, they had better start ploughing a neutral furrow. This direct attack on the morale of G-Division was extremely successful and the quantity and quality of Castle intelligence soon showed a marked deterioration. As previously mentioned, Collins's particularly daring coup in spending an entire night ruffling through the intelligence files was of great importance in laying the foundation for his own counter force in Dublin.

Two other key detective agents on Collins's side were Neligan and McNamara, who rendered immense service to the IRA. The unit of Collins's own troops, in addition to the detectives who were working for him in the Castle, and his own intelligence staff, was what became known as Collins's Squad. Led by Paddy Daly, this was a full-time company of Volunteers who were directly under Collins's personal orders. They were available at all times of the day or night, as directed by the Intelligence Officers. The Squad consisted of Mick McDonnell, Paddy Daly, Bill Stapleton, Jimmy Conroy, Frank Bolster, Paddy Griffiths, Ben Byrne, Johnny Dunne, David Slattery, Mick Kennedy, Eddie Byrne, Vinny Byrne, Mick Kelly and Pat McCree. The rank and file members of the squad were often called the "Twelve Apostles", and as men dropped out, others were added to the list. It is a curious coincidence, nothing more, that Michael Collins' son, Richard Llewelyn Davies, later became a member of an elite group in Cambridge University, which he suggested be named the Twelve Apostles.

The three wings of Collins's organisation worked very well. Major political information and intelligence information was forwarded to Collins through his contacts in the Castle, particularly the four detectives. This was then processed by the Intelligence staff, Tobin, Cullen and the others. When action was decided, usually to eliminate a particular "tout" or spy, this action was carried out by two members of the Squad, operating under the immediate control and identification of the intelligence officer and an extraordinary number of successful assassinations were carried out during the two years that this system was in operation.

The Squad members were under the very strictest discipline; they were to take orders directly from Collins and not to discuss their movements or actions with any other Volunteers, nor to let any other people in the Movement know that they were, in fact, members of the Volunteers, let alone in Collins's squad. They were always readily available, kept together in small groups and they had, at their disposal, a safe house in Upper Abbey Street, and could be, fairly quickly, in any part of the City. The squad and the intelligence staff consisted of what became known as "Collins's Division". It operated entirely on its own apart from the Dublin Brigade of the Volunteers. As the war developed, the Dublin Brigade had their own Active Service Unit, which consisted of, more or less, the same type of workers as were in the Squad, including Charlie Dalton, a tough and brave Volunteer whose elder brother was an officer in the British Army.

During this time, Collins' life was extraordinarily busy and crowded on other fronts. As Minister of Finance, he had led an extremely successful drive to promote and collect an Irish War loan. The target was originally a quarter of a million pounds and this amount was exceeded in a very short space of time. In addition to this, as central figure in the development of the Volunteer war efforts, he was constantly meeting officers from all over, organising the smuggling of arms, processing intelligence reports from all over the country, and in the midst of it, no one seems to know how he possible managed it, he also had a private and personal and emotional life. He continued to lay siege to Kitty Kiernan in Longford, occasionally with visits and sometimes with letters, and it would appear at this stage had definitely set his heart on marrying her. But marriage was a long way in the future. In the meantime there was a war to be fought.

However, an old friend from the past had re-entered his life, Lady Moya Llewellyn-Davis had come to Dublin and had purchased a house in Killester, a very large house called Furry Park, in wooded grounds stretching down the shores of Dublin Bay to the slob lands. Collins frequently visited Lady Moya and occasionally stayed the night there. On most of these occasions, he spent the night in Lady Moya's bed. It was a fairly safe house for Collins. Crompton Llewellyn-Davis was known to be the Solicitor General, an impeccable member of the establishment, Baron in the House of Lords and very often Collins would have been mistaken for a police security officer. The house was quite large and there was a secret passage called the Nuns Walk which led from the back hall down underground and out into the woods from whence the path went down to the shore. One wonders how Collins ever got time to sleep with so many activities upon his mind.

Things got even more complicated when Lady Hazel Lavery acquired a house in Greystones. Sir John was usually in London and Hazel amused herself by flirting with Collins. This soon led to sex, as Michael was a particularly direct person. He would never use his considerable personal magnetism on any of the virtuous virgins of the "Movement", who would be shattered when he inevitably moved on. But this sophisticated and amoral woman was fair game. It is easy to criticise him on this score, but he was a healthy and over-active young man, daily running hideous risks, with the possibility of a few second's notice of a violent death every day. He was certainly taking grave security risks, since Lady Hazel had close links to the core of the British establishment. Some Republican historians have hinted that she was, in fact acting as an agent of Lloyd George. There is no evidence whatever for this. More probably, there was a simple factor of the excitement of dalliance with the handsome and powerful Rebel leader, a Valentino figure, who intrigued Lady Hazel.

EIGHT

The War

Almost as soon as the Republican Government was established, De Valera surprised everyone by declaring that he intended to go to America. For a while, there was considerable disagreement in the ranks of the leadership. De Valera was insistent and eventually Collins made arrangements. De Valera's plan was to work on American public opinion, to collect money for the movement, and to seek to influence President Wilson. Harry Boland was sent over first, to make arrangements and to set up appropriate organisational links with the Irish-Americans. However, his second very important mission on behalf of Collins, was to make arrangements with an American financier called Thomas Fortune-Ryan and the Clan na Gael, for the development of a new guerrilla weapon of enormous power, called the Thompson Submachine Gun. But this was a highly secret operation, not known to any other member of the Irish Government at that time.

Boland's leaving the country at the time had a number of effects. He had had a very firm grip on Sinn Féin, and when he was replaced as Secretary, and his influence as a revolutionary removed from the councils, that organisation reverted back to its old stance of Griffiths, and became much more moderate in its leadership and its opinions. Collins and the IRB did not pay much heed to this at the time, but it was to be of importance later. Boland also, lost out to Collins in the siege of Kitty Kiernan's heart. Although she never made any definite announcement, Collins saw her every two or three weeks, Boland wrote to her every two or three days from America, but Collins was much more persuasive, and in the end, she agreed to marry Collins. But Boland staunchly maintained that this did not affect his friendship and love for Collins and he wished them both well.

With the departure of De Valera, Collins became the dominant figure in the whole of the Republican movement. He held down four important positions in the Army. He was also Minister for Finance, and in effect, the political leader, even though nominally Griffiths was President of the Dáil. Collins engaged himself both in the building up of the intelligence organisation and the assassination squads. He also had responsibility for the importation of arms all over the country and the parcelling out of arms and ammunition amongst all the country brigades. He had the primary job of enthusing the Volunteers into action and he was quite determined that the War would be started and prosecuted as quickly and as vigorously as possible. Under his influence, this was certainly done, and in the next eighteen months, during which De Valera was in America, engaged in the fights and squabbles with the various Irish-American organisations, Collins cast a mighty shadow across the land, and extended the influence of the IRB throughout the movement.

Meanwhile in America, De Valera had succeeded in causing a bitter split amongst the Irish Americans, which doomed his chances of getting the Democratic Party Platform to include support for the Irish Republic. He formed a splinter organisation fiercely anti-IRB and politically ineffective called the American Association for the Recognition of the Irish Republic, AARIR, which was of little use to the struggle at home. TP Coogan succinctly sums up De Valera in America:

> "Irish Americans subscribed a total of $5,123,640 in bond certificates. De Valera only allowed something over half of this to come to Ireland, the rest remaining in American banks from which source he eventually succeeded in getting control of sufficient funds to found what became his family's newspaper empire."

De Valera had arrived in America in June 1919, and almost immediately afterwards, the tension that had existed within the movement, and at Cabinet level, between Michael Collins and the IRB on one hand, and a group of ministers and deputies led by Cathal Brugha, and Austin Stack on the other, increased greatly and threatened the unity of the Cabinet. There seemed to be little profound political differences between them, but the strong personal antipathy arising from Collins's political and sometimes, domineering attitude in Cabinet, was especially resented by Brugha and Stack. Other Cabinet members and other deputies in the Dáil resented Collins's position, by virtue of his membership of the IRB, and were jealous of the support structure which the Brotherhood had provided for him. This would normally have included people like Griffiths, Kevin O'Higgins and others, not specifically Republican, but Nationalist in outlook.

This tension grew, and finally on 20 August 20, Cathal Brugha proposed to the Dáil a resolution which would have a profound effect in outlining the nature of the future split, and which introduced internecine politics and factionalism in the highest level of the movement. He said that the Volunteers should be asked, at the next convention, to swear allegiance to Dáil Eireann and the Government of the Republic. It was also natural that all the members of the Dáil and the Government should swear the same oath, and commit their allegiance to the Republic before the Volunteers were asked to recognise them. This seemed fairly innocuous, in effect, because the Volunteers had not, up to that time, sworn any oath of loyalty to the Dáil, and since that they had predated the general election, the matter had never arisen. But, in Brugha's proposition, every deputy, officer and clerk of the Dáil, and every member of the Volunteers must swear allegiance to the Irish Republic and to the Dáil.

This was not just a minor irritation of bureaucratic intent. The text of the oath was:

> "I, AB, do solemnly swear or affirm, that I do not and shall not yield a
> voluntary support to any pretended government, authority or power
> within Ireland, hostile and inimical thereto. I do further swear or affirm,
> that to the best of my knowledge and ability, I will support the Irish
> Republic and the Government of the Irish Republic, which is Dáil
> Éireann, against all enemies, both foreign and domestic, and will bear
> true faith and allegiance to the same, and I take this obligation freely,
> without any mental reservations or purpose of evasion. So help me, God."

The resolution was seconded by Terence Mac Swiney. Several deputies
opposed it but Arthur Griffith, who had never been notable before for his
support for the Republican principles, spoke in favour of this resolution with
extreme conviction, that he was astonished that the members had not taken an
oath of allegiance at their first meeting; every person there should pledge their
allegiance to the standing Government of Ireland. If they were not a regular
Government, then they were shams and impostors, and also the Army and
Government of a country could not come under a separate authority, where
there would be a possible question as to the form of the oath, as to the necessity of taking the oath. This oath would regularise the situation and if they
were a regularly constituted Government, there would be no question of an
oath of allegiance. The taking of an oath did not preclude one from serving on
local boards and forwarding the interests of the country in such a capacity, and,
he, Griffiths, was absolutely in favour of the motion.

The Dáil, on a division, carried this motion, and adopted the suggested
form of oath. This would appear to be the first indication of that obsession
with oaths and formulas of oaths and the tying of a man's loyalties, which a few
years later, was to be potent factor in the internecine bloodshed, by which the
early years of the 20s are remembered with shame and dishonour. It was the
first attack, covert, upon the organisation and pretensions of the IRB, who of
course, had their own even more sweeping oath to which they gave prec-
edence.

The question of an oath, which appeared on the surface to be a relatively
normal piece of bureaucratic bumbledom, in fact, was a conscious and deliberate attempt to limit the growth and the power of the IRB, and if possible, to
cause dissension within the Brotherhood. The oath then, therefore, went to
be considered by the Executive of the Volunteers. Because of its Army structure, the Volunteers had, in fact, taken a separate oath to the Republic, but not
to the Dáil, and of loyalty to their own Executive who appointed the Headquarters staff, and to whom, in fact, matters of political importance affecting
the Volunteers were always referred. But the Executive and GHQ staff were
mainly "Brothers".

Again, because of the extreme degree of democracy that this involved, it
meant that two years later, when the Treaty came to be considered, the Army

sat down to consider their attitude towards it, and of course, the oath that they were taking on behalf of the Dáil had very little effect.

On the Volunteer Executive, Collins and other influential members, who were members of the IRB, opposed the pledge to the Dáil and maintained that the Volunteer oath to the Republic was enough. They argued, in fact, that there were members of the Dáil who were not in the IRB, and whose loyalty could not be proven, and that the Dáil could easily, some day, compromise the Republican cause, and accept less than the Republic. They would have preferred that the Army would continue to be controlled by its own Executive and by the IRB. However, the majority of members of the Volunteer Executive did not wish to have open disagreement between themselves and the Minister for Defence and the Dáil. They agreed, in order to meet the views of the other members of the Executive, that the IRA Executive would remain in being, and act as an advisory body with the Minister for Defence, and the oath was taken by the Volunteers. But in effect, there was a widening and deepening chasm, between Collins and Brugha, and the Executive of the Volunteers had, by this action, been politicised.

This, of course, referred only to the Volunteers. The IRB remained totally independent and continued whatever oath its members might find it necessary and expedient to take, with their first loyalty to the Brotherhood itself, and their first obedience to its Central Organiser, the Head Centre, Michael Collins, whom they obstinately continued to regard as the true President of the Irish Republic.

Collins was very successful in his efforts to raise the National Loan, even though the British had declared the loan illegal. One of the earliest attempts of the British to prevent the loan from being a success was to import a number of accountants and officials who had power to examine all bank accounts and to seize monies. The chief of these was a Magistrate, Alan Bell, who was a long-established secret agent and a confidante of Lord French. He was a truly efficient and confident person, and he caused Collins a great deal of annoyance in the activity that he conducted in the various head offices of the Dublin banks, examining accounts and asking awkward questions.

In those days, it was a risky business to cause Collins a deal of annoyance, and one day on his way to work on the Merrion Road tram, Alan Bell was taken off the tram by three men and shot dead. This caused the others to have a great deal less enthusiasm about their work and the National Loan was greatly oversubscribed. At the same time, through the close linked network of the IRB, Collins was tending the whole Volunteer organisation, encouraging attacks on barracks and on the RIC, and carrying out his war of attrition against the morale of the G-Division and the various spies of the British that the British had linked throughout the country. He had established a network of workers on the railway and post offices and through his private postal service, he sent any letter he wished throughout the country. After a short time, he was in possession of an enormous amount of information, which was correlated by a dedicated staff. His executive Secretary was a girl called Sinead Mason, who had the task of controlling the flow of sensitive information to the Intelligence Divisional officers. She was a perfect jewel, and like many of the girls in the staff, she was hopelessly in love with Michael. He behaved honourably and never trifled with her emotions.

By the end of 1919, Collins would have been quite happy, living his busy life, working 14 hours a day, ceaselessly weaving the pattern of revolution, conspiring endlessly with the Brotherhood to increase its influence and effectiveness throughout the ranks of the Volunteer Army, and in the meantime, in pursuit of long term objectives, he was wooing the girl he hoped to marry, back in Granard.

But over all, both the military and political situation was proceeding very satisfactorily for the war leader of a tiny country, endeavouring to extricate itself from the strongest Empire in the World. By the early summer, the guerrilla war of the IRA had achieved considerable success. They had almost entirely cleared the countryside, outside of North East Ulster, as far as the smaller villages and towns were concerned, of the Royal Irish Constabulary. All the smaller barracks had been evacuated, promptly to be burned by the IRA, and the constabulary were now concentrated in military barracks in the larger towns, fortified with barbed wire, festooned with sandbags and equipped with machine guns and grenades.

The British military position was quickly deteriorating, and with it the political position, as both in America and Britain and in the old dominions, public opinion began to be made aware of the excesses of the Black-and-Tans and the treatment of, what was regarded as a conquered and subject people by the security forces.

The *Irish Times*, in a trenchant editorial said on 1 May:

> "The Irish Executive must be faced with the full recognition of the dismal truth, that it had hitherto been fighting a losing battle. The forces of the Crown have been driven back on their Headquarters in Dublin, by a steadily advancing enemy. The King's Government has virtually ceased to exist south of the Boyne and west of the Shannon."

This could be a description of the course of almost every classic guerrilla campaign since then. The gradual extension of the campaign throughout the countryside, with the guerrillas occupying, initially the wilder and remote areas, and then the towns and villages, until finally, they would come within striking distance of the Capital itself. This pattern has been followed with great detail, as almost all the successful revolutionary leaders since have carefully studied the tactics and policies of Michael Collins and the Republican Army.

But the Government in Britain felt keenly the need to make some effort to bring the War back on a winning streak for them, to which end, they came to the conclusion that the main problem in Ireland was not so much the total disaffection of the people, whom they foolishly believed could be still recalled to loyalty to the Crown and the Empire; but it was in effect, the malevolent tensions and conspiracies of a tiny number of fanatical Republicans, chief of whom was Michael Collins.

They decided that they should make a determined effort to eliminate the political leadership of the IRB, and thereby reverse, what seemed to be, the inevitable course of history. They were aware that otherwise they would face growing pressure from the more intelligent sections of the British establishment. They could not depend, any longer, on the total loyalty of the popular press and in the leading circles in business and the Institute of Directors. There were warnings that the trouble in Ireland had gone on so long, and was, in fact, increasing with intensity. Once it had ceased to become a policing action, the Government had put pressure on the Imperial General Staff and they decided that a final push would be made to eliminate their main enemies. This was in obedience to a dictum of Field Marshal Sir Henry Wilson, who declared, quite openly that he was totally opposed to the pattern of indiscriminate reprisals and murders that were going on by the security forces, who were out of control. He preferred controlled murder, and, in fact, said quite definitely, that if these people had to be murdered, then the Government should murder them properly. Somewhat to his surprise, he was given just that task.

From the departure of De Valera to America, despite the loss of his good companion, Harry Boland, it might be said that this was the happiest period of Michael Collins's life. He was almost free to supervise the growth and development of every facet of the national struggle. He had the close-knit structure of the Brotherhood through which his orders would be transmitted to every branch of the Army. He had the growing support of the Volunteer movement, and he had the joy of watching the slowly awakening consciousness of the people. He was helped by the reaction of the British, who behaved with their customary arrogant stupidity. To begin, he concentrated on the development of the structure of the Volunteers as a national fighting force and of building up the Intelligence Service. Within those functions, he paralysed the flow of information to the enemy, and above all, he was able to find out who was supplying information to the Castle. In addition, he was also very much involved in the importation of arms and the distribution of supplies throughout the entire network of the Volunteers.

From the beginning, he was quite determined that there would never again be an open military stand up fight, unless the forces would be, at least equal, and this would be a long time in the future. Through the help of a number of indefatigable organisers, he gradually supervised the growth and development of a brigade of the Volunteers in every county, and, of course, Cork had three brigades. In each county, each brigade area was in turn divided up into battalions, covering major local regions, and each battalion had a company structure and in the company would be all the Volunteers of a particular village or town or townland or local government area. It was very much a people's army, each member working most of the time on their normal avocations, and studying the art of guerrilla war and drilling with the IRA for a few hours each week. The Volunteers in a particular company may not have had very much work to do, except possibly, digging trenches on a road or cutting down a tree or blowing up a bridge. Above all, they were constantly engaged in the supply of information on the movements, particularly the regular movements, of the RIC and British Army patrols, preparing for the "War of the Flea and the Dog".

As this structure was developed and improved and extended throughout the country, the second significant development ensued. This was the creation of "Flying Columns", or Active Service Units as they came to be known. Under this system, which reached its highest level of development in the Cork area, there would be 50–100 of the best Volunteers in each brigade, who would be full time, always on the run, moving about from battalion area to battalion area. The personnel would constantly change as men became trained and had some experience and scope, would go back to their village companies and battalion staff and others would take their place. The total number of the column would be controlled, to a certain extent, by the number of rifles that would be available. After this system had been in operation for about six months, it proved to be a highly flexible method of carrying the War to the enemy. They were enormously resilient, capable of absorbing every punch from the enemy without any major military damage to the Volunteer structure or to the overall Republican movement.

When the time was deemed right to the GHQ staff and the Supreme Council of the IRB which fairly closely identified with each other, the next phase of the War began. The Volunteer companies burned various barracks and building which the British would probably occupy as barracks. They began attacking outlying RIC barracks, partly with the intention of driving the garrison out, and to that extent, reclaiming the particular area for the people, but also with the ever present intention of securing arms for the next days battle. Within a short time, this was highly successful. The Royal Irish Constabulary withdrew to the main towns. The Constabulary had always been a semi-military organisation, they were always trained in arms and carried carbines and revolvers, and were much less a police force than an occupation force. The intensity of the IRA attacks on the Constabulary increased. They became more and more identified in people's minds as an enemy. They became more and more, as De Valera had suggested, boycotted, socially ostracised and after a very short period, there were absolutely no recruits coming into the Constabulary from the population as a whole. They could not shop in their locality, or drink in local pubs, and, increasingly, had to travel to another district for Sunday Mass, or else parade in armed formation.

The typical example of this was when about April 1919, the Cork 2nd Brigade, then under the leadership of Liam Lynch, who was also a member of the Supreme Council of the IRB, made a successful attempt on Araglen Barracks and burned it to the ground. The following September, they had almost run out of targets, to the extent that the first formal and organised and planned operation against the British Military Army itself, since 1916, occurred when his flying column surrounded and disarmed a party of 15 British soldiers in Fermoy. Gradually, the RIC became almost useless as an intelligence force. As a police force, they had already lost control of the people, and paralleling the rise of the new State within the old State, the ordinary people were paying very little attention to the RIC with regard to normal policing.

This was particularly evident during the second half of 1919, by which time the Republican courts, the Sinn Féin Courts as they were called, became widespread throughout the country. These were usually headed by a tribunal in each county, consisting of the Sinn Féin deputy, the O/C of the local brigade and whatever other prominent personalities who would be trusted and respected by the people. Once these courts were established and met regularly, they proved to be an extraordinarily potent weapon against the Empire. Ordinary people went to the Irish Courts, which sat, and proceeded with a great lack of formality. They were intent in matters of dispute, on getting to the facts of the case, proceeding on a basis of justice rather than law, and their decisions were respected and obeyed without question.

No doubt, the fact that they had behind them the ultimate military sanction of the IRA had a lot to do with it, but more so was the fact that they seemed to be transparently fair. The other side of the coin was that the British courts were deserted, and no one would dare to take a case in them, and no one would appear to defend one. And the farcical situation was, that in the middle of a revolution, when the authority of the Government was defied, and the controls clearly crumbling, the number of justices or judges and assizes, who brandished white gloves and declared that there was a complete lack of crime throughout the area.

This had a tremendous effect upon the morale of the Anglo-Irish who formed the main elements of the magistracy, the local Justice of the Peace and so forth, so by early 1920, 186 resigned their commissions. They felt that they had lost the confidence of the people in the district, they were being used to dispense justice, and they felt that it would be better if they did not attempt to pretend that they still exhibited this authority. These mass resignation were a tremendous blow to the prestige of the Government and to the morale of the administration. It also secured their place in the affections of the local people. Many subsequently joined the Sinn Féin legal administration, and practised in local Irish Courts as barristers and magistrates.

It is difficult to exaggerate the political effect of the Republican Courts on the general course of entire struggle. The were the most visible part of the new State that was being created, under the skin of the old, and people generally came into contact with the Republic firstly through the Courts. There was soon an ambivalence in the attitude of the RIC, many of the most thoughtful of whom were thinking that the Republic would win, and their future depended upon a friendly neutrality.

An even greater blow to the Castle administration came in January 1920, when the local government elections were held throughout the country. Candidates of the Republican movement, under the banner of Sinn Fein, fought every constituency everywhere, and the results were quite astonishing, indicating that the "Khaki" Election result of December 1918, was certainly not a flash in the pan.

Of 12 city and borough councils through the country, eleven declared for the Republic, and only Belfast did not have a Sinn Féin majority. In Ulster, five counties had a Sinn Féin majority and four Unionist. Also in Ulster, 23 towns voted Sinn Féin, with 22 voting Unionist. Sinn Féin had 172 majorities out of 226 county and local councils. In effect, the majority of local government was now in the people's hands. From all over the country, these councils now passed formal resolutions that they would, henceforth, ignore the Castle administration, and pledged allegiance to the Republic and Dáil Eireann. All official relations with the British Government and with the Local Authority Board at the Castle were broken off by 80 per cent of the Irish local authorities. The Government of the Dáil was the sole authority recognised by the people throughout Ireland.

The flagship resolution was one passed by Dublin Corporation: "Accordingly this council of the elected representatives in the City of Dublin, hereby acknowledges the authority of Dáil Éireann to be the duly elected Government of the Irish people, and undertakes to give effect to all legislation by the said Dáil Éireann, in so far as it effects this Council." The voting on this resolution was 38 in favour, five against. All the other major cities and towns, with the exception of Belfast, were similar.

This was a massive blow to the British, and at this stage it could have been foreseen, that quite clearly, the Irish were going to win the shooting war. However, the war had not yet formally began. There had been practically no involvement of British troops since 1916, and the RIC, who were by now were almost useless as an instrument of repression, had been the main target. Quite soon after the local election results, the British troops began to be the focus of more Volunteer activity, particularly in Dublin. Ambushes and attacks upon the British, sniping on barracks and attacks on Army lorries were frequent. The Government in London decided to enlarge the scope of the combat, and on the advice of Sir Henry Wilson, attempted to convey the impression to the world that this was entirely a police matter rather than a military one, and they organised two paramilitary forces to be sent to Ireland.

One of these forces was known as the Black-and-Tans, because of the mixture of uniforms that they wore, and they became known as a by-word of cruelty, stupidity and repression unequalled until the SS marched into France in 1940. The other was a force of ex-officers, who were recruited, primarily, to take the offensive against the IRA. They were called the Auxiliaries. They were fairly highly paid, extremely well armed and totally out of control. In battle they were very brave, and the IRA treated them with great respect.

After the arrival of these new forces reinforcing the RIC, the role of the British Army was reduced, mainly, to roadblocks and guards on major buildings. The progress of the shooting war accelerated and a number of casualties on both sides hit the headlines. One in particular caused a great deal of personal pain to Michael Collins, arising from an ambush in Dublin. An attack upon a military patrol led to the capture of a young Volunteer, Kevin Barry. He was 17 years of age, in his first year as a medical student in University College Dublin. Barry was promptly sentenced to death and grossly maltreated. Despite a tremendous campaign throughout England and America to have the sentence of death revoked, Barry was eventually hanged not long after his eighteenth birthday, and on the two nights before he was hanged, he had been tortured by having his arms twisted and punched severely, to give them the names of the other members of the battalion flying column, of which he was a member before his arrest. This is the first time it is known that the Security Forces used the name of Michael Collins in an interrogation.

With Barry's arms twisted behind his back, he was taunted. They said: "Where is your Michael Collins now. What can he do for you?", to which Barry replied, "He can do nothing for me now, but I can die for him" and the next morning he did. It had a tremendous effect on both the Irish people and the supporters of the Republican movement. One of the prison staff present later reported this to Liam Tobin, who reported it to Collins, and it is said that he broke down and cried with bitter frustration at the death of this young boy. "The poor kid" he sobbed.

But the War went on and grew in intensity. With the Black-and-Tans on the scene, and the Auxiliaries, a new and more sinister element of personal assassination ensued. Prominent Republicans , deputies in the Dáil, mayors of cities, were all liable to be murdered. The Lord Mayor of Cork was Tomas McCurtain, and on one particular night, the district in which he lived was entirely surrounded by RIC, a curfew had been proclaimed, and a number of armed men with their faces blackened, smashed the door of his house down and murdered him on front of his wife. He was immediately replaced by Terence MacSwiney, who was to die on hunger strike after 72 days. The Mayor of Limerick was murdered and a number of other councillors and important political persons. It became the normal practice for the Tans and the Auxiliaries to murder prisoners when they were able to catch people after an ambush or any military action of any description. It was very rare, in fact, that the Tans took prisoners back to barracks alive.

Despite the military campaign and the daily war going on, the Dáil administration continued to preserve and extend the structure of the embryo State. In almost all circumstances, they were opposed, with the upmost ferocity, by the forces of the Crown. The Dáil had established a Commission on Irish industrial resources and the members of this Commission were to meet on 21 January 1920, in Cork City, to enquire into national resources, the present condition of manufacturing, production and industries in Ireland. The

Commission had, in fact, arranged to take evidence, on the subject of milk and milk products, fisheries, electricity and power, and had been invited by the Lord Mayor and the Corporation to hold the meetings in the City Hall in Cork. When the Commission arrived they found the City Hall and every public building in Cork in the possession of armed troops, who rudely and forcibly prevented their session. The Commission met, however, and transacted their business in a private house. This pattern was repeated throughout the country, wherever the British had advance notice of any official action taken on behalf of the Dáil or Local Government or any part of the Republican administration.

NINE

The Rise of Emmet Dalton

1920 had opened with spectacular political successes for the Republic, with the results of the local elections throughout the country, which sounded the death-knell of British rule in Ireland. This major political advance was the main agency and motor of the continual building up of the separate national administration, at all levels from the central government of Dáil Éireann down to the Urban and Rural District Councils. This was the visible appearance of the phenomenon of "Dual Power"; one external and attempting to impose itself by military force and repression – the other, native and popular, growing slowly and tentatively as the people developed confidence in themselves and in their own native government.

The glamorous headlines all over the world, the tales of ambushes, guerrilla fighters and flying columns, of Black-and-Tans, hunger strikes and jailbreaks, were the froth on the top of the struggle, newsworthy, but not of nearly as much significance as the steady denuding of British influence, and the growing attachment and loyalty of the Irish people to the people's own government.

The British were still formally in possession. They garrisoned all the military barracks, they ruled Dublin Castle, the focus of their administration for 600 years. They had all the physical trappings and attributes of conquerors, but in their hearts they were uneasy, knowing that the future was uncertain. They took comfort in the vast web of vested interests, the supporters and people who had a traditional, ancestral loyalty to the Empire, and especially in the network of ex-soldiers, informers and agents that the Empire had patiently built up over the centuries. An important factor in strengthening the British position was the pivotal information, pressure, and executive action of two of the most effective double agents in history – Emmet Dalton and Tim Healy.

Born in Dublin in 1898 to parents who could be described as Redmondite, although the phrase did not become relevant for many years, young Emmet Dalton joined the British Army in 1914, whenever the Irish Parliamentary Party Leader, John Redmond, called upon his supporters to fight for the freedom of small nations. He was soon promoted to corporal and in that capacity displayed courage and leadership, and a rare appreciation of the military position in the trenches in Flanders. When the officer in charge of his unit was killed, Corporal Dalton took over command of the Company, without authorisation, rallied his disorganised forces and repelled the German attack. He was decorated for his bravery and was promoted to the commissioned ranks. His superiors in the Army had a high opinion of him, and he advanced rapidly. Within a few years, he was appointed ADC to General Sir Henry Wilson, later the Field Marshal in command of the Imperial General Staff.

There soon grew a very deep personal friendship between Captain Dalton and the General, most extraordinary because Wilson had a thinly-disguised hatred towards most things Irish and Catholic, and later played a prominent part in organising the Orange pogroms in Belfast.

For this, he headed the list of "undesirables" in Michael Collin's deadly field notebook. Dalton left the Army with the rank of Major.

His younger brother Charley became a member of the Dublin Brigade of the Volunteers, and by 1919, was a trusted member of the Active Service Unit, and friendly with Michael Collins, whom he admired greatly. Charley Dalton was a man of enormous physical courage, and on one occasion, when he was challenged by a trio of drunken Black-and-Tans in Dame Street, he drew his pistol, shot one and chased the others for a considerable distance.

Shortly after Major Dalton returned home, his brother Charley was arrested by the Security Forces. Major Dalton took a cab to the Castle in full regimentals and succeeded in obtaining the release of his brother. Charley Dalton had been engaged in some celebrated gunfights in the streets of Dublin with the G-Division detectives and later with the Black-and-Tans, in which he showed a bull-headed heroism, a level of courage that was greatly commented upon, and there is little doubt that as a fairly simple minded figure, he was an important and wholehearted soldier of the Dublin Brigade. In later years, he wrote a book called *With the Dublin Brigade*, which was ghost-written for him by Moya Llewellyn-Davis. He later played a prominent part in the Free State Army mutiny of Collins loyalists in 1924, which marked the last act in the drama of the IRB.

No doubt, by sheer coincidence, when Major Dalton returned to his family home with his young brother, one of the casual visitors there was Kathleen Napoli-McKenna, who was a close aide to Michael Collins both in the Department of Intelligence and in the Department of Finance. To her, Dalton said, that if he had realised the position of the Irish in Dublin was so bad, he would have been fighting in Ireland and not in France. Kathleen McKenna considered this and later mentioned to Collins that Emmet Dalton would be prepared to help. Within a few days he was taken to meet Collins, who questioned him about his past record in the Army and his military experience. Dalton did not mention that he had, in fact, been Aide de Camp to Sir Henry Wilson, but agreed to work for Collins and joined the Dublin Brigade. He was involved in a celebrated attempt to raid Mountjoy Prison to rescue General Sean MacEoin, the famous blacksmith from Ballinalee, who was awaiting trial for murder. Collins did not appear to know that this particular attempt was to be made, and apparently was rather annoyed about it.

British State Papers released in 1990, included two letters relating to the case. One was from Sir John Anderson, the political supremo of Lloyd-George in the Castle, to General McCready, Chief of Security, complaining about the lack of security on the day in Mountjoy. What had happened was that Dalton and another Volunteer Officer dressed in British Uniforms. They then captured a British armoured car, suspiciously easily and drove up to Mountjoy with fake papers and demanded that the prisoner MacEoin be handed over to them to bring to the Castle.

The armoured car was stopped between two locked gates and the attempted escape probably would have been successful except that the alarm was raised and the raiding party succeeded in fighting their way out, although they were inside the prison at the time. It was very clear from the circumstances of the attempted escape that was there no possibility whatever of MacEoin having been rescued and it was extraordinary that apparently they had permitted the armoured car to escape from the prison, which required collusion from the prison staff. The escape attempt, however, did confirm the bona fides, the bravery and the ability of Emmet Dalton in the minds of the Dublin Brigade and of Collins, and from then on he was a trusted officer of the Brigade, and was later promoted to GHQ Staff.

The second important paper, released in 1990, from General McCready to Sir John Anderson, indicated that there was never any chance of the prisoner being rescued because he knew in advance of everything that was to happen, and key members of the Prison staff had been briefed. There was no doubt whatever that the rescue was a fake and was never intended to go through, but it served another purpose, that of confirming Dalton's bona fides.

Less that a fortnight later, the greatest defeat of the Volunteers in the entire War happened, when the British surprised the Dublin Brigade on a massive raid on the Customs House, the main tax collecting centre in Ireland. The Brigade lost six men dead and 80 were captured, with very large quantities of guns and ammunition. It was a severe blow to the morale and assets of the Dublin Brigade.

It emerged later that Emmet Dalton had taken an important part in training discussions with the Dublin Brigade and on the planning of the raid on the Customs House, which became a trap. Following his service as ADC to Sir Henry Wilson, Dalton had entered British Intelligence and he was to remain in either MI5, MI6 or the SAS, transferring from one to the other, for approximately 30 years. He was the most potent spy the British had ever had in Ireland.

Following the death of Michael Collins, in which Emmet Dalton played an important part as facilitator. Dalton, for a brief period of time, was Officer Commanding the Cork Division of the Free State Army. However, he found it very difficult to retain his military career, in view of the open hostility and suspicion that greeted him almost every time he entered an Officers' Mess. For some time, there were shouts and jeers of "Who shot Collins?". Dalton began to drink very heavily at this period and the Free State Government thought it advisable to relieve him of military duties. They appointed him to a sinecure office, under which they could keep him in close supervision, as Clerk of the new Free State Seanad. However, his drinking got worse and his general character deteriorated and after a short period, he left Ireland. From the mid 1920s, Dalton went back into active service with MI5 in a staff capacity, working in photography and film work. He became friendly with another MI5 operator called Chadwick, who had lived at Bankside, Walford Road in Herts. and he lodged in Chadwick's house. Micheal O'Cuinneagáin records, in his book *On the Arm of Time* a visit by a researcher, probing into Dalton's background:

In Dalton's memoirs, which were left in the possession of Mrs Chadwick, there was a small piece of paper being a receipt from the London branch of a Scottish Bank, £6,500 in 1926. The address of the bank and the date of the receipt were given by the researcher, but the name of the account holder was not on the receipt. The memoirs contained a reference to a reward for Collins's assassination because of his alleged connection with the assassination of Sir Henry Wilson in 1922. Quote: "While I did not pull the trigger, I saw no reason why I could not collect the reward." Curiously, Mrs Chadwick allowed the researcher to read the memoirs, but not to make notes or photocopies.

There is no information available as to Dalton's activities in the period from about 1930 to the beginning of the War in 1939, when he again surfaced as a part-time photographer for MI5 and was also apparently living as a professional gambler.

The second major British agent was Tim Healy, who in the course of his treacherous career spanning almost 45 years, moved from being a minor spy for the British to being the Governor General of the Irish Free State. The pseudonym by which Healy was known in Dublin Castle was Thorp and it first appears in the Castle intelligence files back in 1882 at the time of the murders of Chief Secretary Burke and Lord Henry Cavendish in the Phoenix Park by the Invincibles, a tiny group of terrorists, which had the effect of outraging English opinion and dashing Home Rule from Parnell's grasp.

The murders were known to have been carried out by a splinter group of the Fenians, who had despaired of its apparently slow and peaceful organisation. This group called themselves the Invincibles. They were quickly caught and sent to the gallows by an informer called Carey, the Invincibles being penetrated by informers. Carey later featured in a *cause celebre* when he was murdered on a liner off the coast of South Africa by a Donegal Fenian called Pat O'Donnell, who was acquitted of the murder on a technicality, it being proved that Carey would have lived had there not been very incompetent surgery. O'Donnell was hanged anyway under anti-Fenian laws for possession of arms and attempted murder.

With the passing of time, rumours began to circulate in Dublin that the real informer was not Carey, but the person whose pseudonym was Thorp. In 1922, shortly before his death, Collins asked Thomas Markham, his chief informant in the Castle, to check on the intelligence papers going back to the period for information regarding the betrayer of the "Invincibles". When the British handed over Dublin Castle to Collins in 1922, they took the precaution of removing all the current intelligence files, but those that were prior to the end of the century, were regarded by them as mere historical information and were not touched. Over the course of his search, Markham came across startling information.

Thorp was in fact Tim Healy, who was then still a trusted advisor of the Free State Government, and who had been present in London during the Treaty negotiations. He was an uncle of Kevin O'Higgins, and after Collins death, became the first Governor General of the Free State, and during all the time from his youth, he had spied on behalf of the Empire, in a senior political capacity. He had literally changed Irish history, having succeeded with his vicious tongue in overthrowing Parnell, when he was on the point of victory. At the time of the murders of Burke and Cavendish in the Phoenix Park, Healy, then a young aspiring lawyer, had been a member of the IRB, and probably also an intimate or member of the Invincibles since the IRB certainly kept a link and informant in that organisation.

In that capacity, he had returned with an important emissary from Clan na Gael in America to Jury's Hotel, there to surprise the proprietor, Captain Jury, who was a known British agent, searching through the luggage of the Clan emissary. In a way in which is yet unclear, they managed to kill Captain Jury by either forcing him to drink poison or by injecting poison. In any event, Jury died. The Clan emissary immediately escaped and went back to America, but Healy was promptly arrested. The Castle then had a choice to make. Young Healy was of a class and ability totally different from the rest of the Fenian prisoners, most of whom were working men from Dublin, and could be hanged or shot without any compunction. But Healy, with his legal training, could be more useful to them if they turned him and got him to work on their side. They gave him an offer he could not refuse. He would either work for the Empire or he would be hanged for the murder of Jury.

This information is both sensational and surprising and requires some background information before it can be accepted as factual. However, Tim Pat Coogan has described the finding of a death certificate for Henry James Jury, Hotel Proprietor, certified as having died from typhus fever five days uncertified on 28 May 1882 in Donnybrook in Dublin. This looks very much like a legal cover up. The interesting thing about the death certificate is that it bears three different dates, the death is registered on the 22nd, certified as having occurred on the 28th, but there is a note on the certificate saying that the typhus was certified as having being existed for eight days and four hours on the 29th. For some reason, in order to preserve the fact that Healy had not been charged with the murder, this fake death certificate saying that Jury had in fact died from typhus was allowed into the public domain. This all occurred approximately a fortnight after the Phoenix Park murders.

In the rush to the evacuation of the Castle, the damaging papers with details of the payments to Healy, were left to be discovered by Markham. Within hours of the news of Collins's death reaching Dublin, someone opened his own private safe in Portobello Barracks and removed all the documents relating to Healy/Thorp, and of course, they have since disappeared. At this time, Healy's nephew, Kevin O'Higgins, had become the strong man of the Provisional Government.

Healy's other great service to the Empire was the destruction of Parnell and his Party and the continuous series of divisive and disruptive activities which he had pursued for 30 years after, and of course, during the protracted and arduous negotiations for the Treaty, Healy hung like a black vulture around the Irish delegation, cajoling, pressing and encouraging and on every possible occasion, sapping their confidence and encouraging them to accept the British draft of the Treaty. For this and because of his cordial business relationships with Winston Churchill and Lloyd George and the key position of his nephew, Kevin O'Higgins, he was rewarded by being appointed the first Governor General of the Irish Free State, elbowing Lady Lavery out of the promised niche in the Vice-Regal Lodge.

The Healy family had always been prominent on the legal stage and had accumulated considerable wealth, including an estate in the West Indies and a considerable investment portfolio in Britain and America.

TEN

Cairo and After

Cairo – 20 July 1920: The whole top floor of Shepheard's Hotel was sealed tight as a mouse's ear and at the bottom of the main stairs a table was pulled across. A fiercely moustachioed sergeant major sat at the table with a lieutenant checking very carefully the credentials of all who passed. Behind him two soldiers with fixed bayonets were on sentry and on the back stairs there were two other soldiers on sentry; on a top landing, a third soldier, all with fixed bayonets.

Inside the main conference, the carefully selected Officers took their seats. An officer, with Colonel's tabs, who sat at the top table called them to attention. The door of an ante-room opened and a tall familiar figure entered. The officers were shocked and surprised. "Attention for the Chief of Staff." The officers stood and saluted. Field Marshal Sir Henry Wilson, Chief of the Imperial General Staff, strode to the front table. Something very big was afoot.

They had been carefully selected from all over the Empire for a secret, possibly dangerous, highly important job, and sent under conditions of strict secrecy to Cairo, some on a destroyer from Gibraltar, several had come through Singapore and India and a shaky military transport flight across the Iraqi Desert, through Mesopotamia and southern Arabia and across the Red Sea. If Sir Henry himself was here it must be very big indeed. They looked with new interest at the officer at the table who had introduced himself as Colonel Charteris of Military Intelligence. Sir Henry began to speak first. He outlined the threat to the Empire caused by the rebellion in Ireland which was proving extremely difficult to put down. As he proceeded he got more emotional and in the end he was quite worked up into a tirade.

"At first this was purely a military matter. We could easily have crushed these tribal people. The Irish have never been difficult to defeat because of their own dissension and the closeness of the homeland. But this time, it is not a military threat alone and the military threat is not the most serious side of it. The Irish have been purporting to set up a new administration of courts, of taxes, of offices of local government to which they have gradually been forced to give their allegiance and to the murders and assassins who call themselves the IRA, the army of the so-called Irish Republic, and they have an illegal assembly comprised of members of Parliament who were elected to sit in the Commons and advise the King and these traitors have set up an illegal assembly which we are hunting down relentlessly. But the mainspring of the resistance to the forces of Law and Order in Ireland is a combination of the military and political. The menace is concentrated on a few, a tiny few, number of extremely capable murderers. The head of these is one Michael Collins.

Your mission, Gentlemen, is to hunt down this group of murderers and to destroy them in the streets of the Capital itself, to clear the way for His Majesty's Forces to bring peace to Ireland. You are to shoot Collins and his number two murderer, Richard Mulcahy, and Richard McKee, who styles himself as commandant of the Dublin Brigade, and Peadar Clancy, who is his adjutant. If we wipe out these four men, we will have crushed the heart of the rebel conspiracy in Dublin. Colonel Charteris will give you details of other targets and of the operational area. You are not to skulk in barracks, you are to live out amongst the people in safe houses, selected by Charteris, and you are to patrol the streets, incessantly, and always armed, and you will drink in public houses, listening to the people, and stopping everyone you see on a bicycle who resembles Collins. You will always have details of military dispositions and there will always be armed soldiers within call. But you are the fighting spearpoint of the Empire in this campaign. You must shoot first, and shoot to kill. You will be in receipt of all intelligence information from all sources, but you will tell no-one of your plans or locations, in particular, you will *not* frequent Dublin Castle, the Police or Military Headquarters, which are riddled with Collins's spies. If a detective goes to the lavatory in the Castle, Michael Collins pulls the chain. You will report daily to Colonel Ormonde Winter, and to him only.

The mainstay of this whole infamous rebel conspiracy is a murderous secret society calling itself the IRB, or the Fenian Brotherhood. We have identified many of the members of this nest of traitors who have fomented murder in His Majesty's Realm for over 60 years. You will execute any of these vipers you come across and thereby do great service to the Empire."

His voice went on rising to a crescendo of hatred as he described what would happen to the Empire if the IRA murderers succeeded in creating their campaign of terror and he promised rewards and promotion in addition to the £10,000 pounds on the head of Collins and Mulcahy. There would be promotion for every officer and there would be total security and indemnification against any action in court if civilians were killed or wounded, or if any other difficulty arose in the pursuit of their military duty They were not to be made amenable to any law.

Colonel Charteris gazed out the window into the flyblown dusk of Cairo. Casually he stretched his arms before him on the table and his glance fell, as if by accident, on the tiny blue scar on his right thumb. His mind was on a distant hot hazy summery evening in West Cork, two boys with their heads touching, as they each repeated the brotherhood oath of Alexander and Ptolemy from over two thousand years ago.

Sir Henry withdrew and the officers were soon settling down to question and discuss the programme for the next four days. It was quite intensive. They had to study maps of the city of Dublin between the two canals, a brief history of the City, a run down of all the major personages and people, all the military positions, all the sources from where they would be expecting support and help. Most of all they studied in detail the pictures and descriptions of Collins, of Mulcahy, of McKee and Clancy, and of many other prominent Republican deputies who were to be shot on sight.

After four intensive days the officers knew more about Dublin than they knew about their own native cities and were like greyhounds waiting to be unleashed. Their mission was to crush the Brotherhood, and they were confident. They were not to go near the Castle, but to report to Colonel Ormonde Winter daily, either at the appropriately named Cairo Cafe, or at Kidds Restaurant. To confuse everyone, they called themselves the Cairo Group. The Squad called them the Cairo Gang.

The next morning they embarked on a destroyer for the first part of the journey home which would take them to Gibraltar for a change of ships, and from there to Southampton. Within a week they would be dispersed in lodgings, carefully selected, throughout respectable districts of Dublin. All the arrangements were made by Colonel Charteris. He gave the details to his Second in Command, Major McMahon, and sent a copy of his report to Sir Henry's secretary at the War Office. A second copy was sent, very briefly, initialled "Lieut. G", for the eyes of Michael Collins, who destroyed it immediately after making some notes in his own field notebook.

Collins behaved with a certain formality. As Director of Intelligence, he presented the files on the officers to Cathal Brugha, Minister of Defence. Brugha received each, and agreed to Collins' proposed actions. Collins, wearing his hat as Director of Operations, arranged with the "12 Apostles", Byrne, Cullen, Thornton, Tobin, Charlie Dalton and seven others, to take appropriate action. It was to be a joint operation, Collins's Squad plus the full resources of the Active Service Unit of The Dublin Brigade.

Within three days the Cairo Officers had acclimatised to Dublin and the following weekend they drew first blood. Two senior officers of the Dublin Brigade, Commandant General Richard McKee and Adjutant Peadar Clancy were betrayed by a tout and arrested together with a Clare volunteer, Conor Clune. They were immediately imprisoned in Dublin Castle and they were interrogated for the first of three interrogations, being tied naked on top of mess tables. Interrogation consisted mainly of burning the prisoners about the legs and genitals with cigarette butts, and twisting their arms behind their backs.

Conon Clune knew nothing, and despite all the ill-treatment, couldn't give them any information. Clancy and McKee bore the weight of a terrible knowledge, which at all costs, they must keep from their captors. On the night of Saturday, 19 September, Ireland's cross was indeed carried by these two men, alone and without hope, in the citadel of the enemy.

The next morning, Sunday 20th, was bright and cold, Dublin was busy early. From early dawn trains and buses were arriving as it was the day of the

All-Ireland Final. It was the day also that the Active Service Unit and Michael Collins's Squad were very busy. The executions started about nine o'clock in the morning in Merrion Square and by 10.30, the campaign had concluded. Fourteen of the sixteen Intelligence Officers recruited in Cairo lay dead, only two escaped; Major McMahon had been called to England and Colonel Charteris, who had chosen to go that weekend to make a personal report to Sir Henry.

As the news spread around Dublin, there was panic in the ranks of those who supported the British connection. Dozens of taxis and hansom cars arrived at Dublin Castle with men throwing together a few precious possessions, desperately seeking shelter and protection. Several were spies whom the IRA didn't even know about. But their existence and names were carefully noted as they entered the Castle and demanded protection.

That afternoon the City was cloaked in fear. The All Ireland Football match began with the Tipperary team entering the field to the tune of the Artane Boys Band. Just then the first of twelve lorryloads of troops and police arrived, and trailing the others were Black-and-Tans. The gates were quickly secured. The Tans drove through onto the barrier fronting the field. It was said afterwards they were supposed to be searching for arms. At a signal they opened fire indiscriminately with rifles and a machine gun. The Tipperary goalkeeper, Hogan, was first to die and twelve others in the crowd died almost instantly, 28 were severely wounded and a several hundred slightly wounded and injured, as the crowd stampeded in fear to escape death. It was called Bloody Sunday.

That night, the final interrogation of Clune, Dick McKee and Peadar Clancy took place in Dublin Castle. The next day their three bodies were handed over to their relatives. They had been "shot while attempting to escape".

The men were quite unrecognisable, their faces burned and blackened, their arms were dislocated, their tortures had been immense and unbearable, but they had not spoken. On Monday 22nd, the bodies were taken to the Pro-Cathedral in Marlborough Street. In the evening a number of men came, including Michael Collins in full Volunteer Uniform, and reverently laid out the bodies of the dead Officers, who were clothed in Volunteer Uniforms and were placed in the coffins. The lids were placed on the coffins and Collins stood the first hour in a guard of honour. All that night, four volunteers stood by each coffin, until the next morning when the requiem mass commenced. During the night there was the usual curfew and the lorries roaring up and down O'Connell Street could clearly be heard. But homage was paid to McKee and Clancy. Collins turned all his resources on the hunt for the spy who had fingered McKee and Clancy. Two days later, "Shankers" Byrne was shot in the North Strand.

The Cairo stunt was the last throw for official state terrorism in Dublin, and when, two days later, Lloyd-George answered the King's summons, he did so like a beaten dog. His Majesty was brief and incisive, "I'm sorry to see, Prime Minister, that things have got worse. You now have no choice. I direct you to explore the possibility of peace in Ireland and we must have peace at the earliest possible moment." Lloyd-George bowed his head and submitted to the inevitable.

Feelers for a truce went out within a week, and Lloyd-George had his first frustrating exchange with the formidable President of Sinn Féin, Eamon De Valera. It was the first step on a long and convoluted road towards the Truce that was still over six months away. Lloyd George persued an ambivalent and duplicitous policy, warmly embracing any approach from self-appointed publicity seekers, and using any opportunity to promote fissures in Sinn Fein, whilst rejecting and pretending not to hear any official statement from the Irish government. But in the end all he could do was delay the inevitable. The British were compelled to recognise that they had lost the political and diplomatic war, with the disciplined phalanx of the great majority of the Irish people. On the military front they could make no headway against the IRA, and could only contemplate either a defeat in the guerrilla war, or a massive escalation of the conflict using tanks and naval forces and aerial bombardment, which was politically impossible on the home front. Having realised that they were losing the war, they set up a secret cabinet committee aimed at devising strategies for winning the Peace, by the tried and trusted tactics of divide and conquer.

ELEVEN

The Thompson Gun

By mid-1920, one of the most ambitious schemes of the Brotherhood began to come to fruition. This was no less than the development and production of a major new weapon of tremendous assistance to guerrilla warfare. The new weapon had, in fact, been under design and development for several years in America. But the impetus to bring it to production came directly from the Brotherhood through its American associates, Clan na Gael. It became known to history as the Thompson sub-machine gun, the "Tommy Gun".

In 1916, a retired Lieutenant Colonel of the American Army called Marcellus Thompson formed a small arms company of his own, designed to develop an automatic rifle. It was based upon the recoil principal which simplified the mechanism rather than the gas cylinder and piston system of most machine guns. Thompson's partner was a well known financier named Thomas Fortune Ryan, who in addition to his interests in high finance was an influential member of the Council of Clan na Gael.

Thompson's plans for his automatic rifle were postponed when America entered the War and he went back into the Army, but by the end of the War in 1918, he returned to his first love in a company called the Auto Ordnance Corporation, which was largely financed by the Brotherhood, unknown to Thompson. There were significant modifications made to the original invention of the recoil rifle and in fact by the end of the development period they had 285 patents relating to small arms manufacture. The gun, which was an object of keen interest to the IRB, was a very short barrelled automatic rifle with a detachable stock. It could be fired with single or automatic bursts from a magazine and the magazine could be flat, holding 20 cartridges or a circular drum holding 50. The important thing was that the ammunition was .45 pistol ammunition of which there were vast quantities available and this was a strong point in the sales. As far as the Brotherhood were concerned an even better point was the fact that the guns, if they were successfully developed, would be ideal for guerrilla warfare and subversive use, both in town and country. With its detachable stock the gun could be easily carried in an overcoat or raincoat. The gun was simple in operation and it had very few moving parts. There was only one critical one, a bronze piece known as the H-piece and it had the slight disadvantage that if it was inserted upside-down the gun wouldn't fire. But otherwise, the cocking and firing arrangements were extremely simple.

The Thompson Gun was quite inaccurate at its extreme range of five to six hundred yards, but at short range was one of the deadliest weapons ever invented. It carried an enormous shock power, or impact, from the heavy 45 calibre cartridges, much greater than the standard .303 rifle as used by all sides in the Great War.

By 1920, the development of this gun proceeded apace, with frequent reports to Michael Collins back in Dublin. One of the most important tasks that Harry Boland had to accomplish in New York, was to take over the financial end of the development of the Thompson gun and to provide the money for a thousand guns at over $220 a piece with adequate supplies of magazines and ammunition. A lot of the Dáil Éireann funds were quietly channelled through the Brotherhood agent in New York, a man called Larry Delacey from Wexford, who became prominent later as the link man between Stephen Hayes, the later Chief of Staff of the IRA and the Fianna Fáil Government.

Delacey worked extremely hard to expedite the development of the Thompson gun. The first two guns were sold by March of 1921. Sean Nunan and Larry Delacey tried them out in the New York 69th Regimental Armoury. They had an exciting evening firing bursts of the different types of magazines. They were greatly impressed by the power of the new gun.

The next week they ordered five hundred guns and several thousand magazines and an ample supply of ammunition. A few early production guns began to trickle into Delacey's hands and several were sent to Ireland for trial. Delacey and Dan Fitzgerald from Kerry, another Brotherhood member, made arrangements to warehouse a large consignment of guns for a major shipment of arms. The Thompson guns, by this stage, had been given out to production by the Colt Arms Company, and almost every gun manufactured by Colt went directly to Larry Delacey through the Auto Ordnance Corporation. The Clan had a warehouse in the Bronx and Delacey begin to store the production line of Thompson guns in crates in this warehouse. By the end of May he had 400 Thompson machine-guns and had planned a shipment as soon as he had 500. At the time there was a dock strike in New York and it was quite possible to have the ships moving in and out without normal papers. There were Brothers at every critical link in the chain.

At Pier 2, in New York Harbour, across the river from the Bronx, a freighter called the *East Side*, in which the Clan had an interest, had been tied up since April. They planned to sail on 17 June. At that time, 495 Thompson sub-machine-guns, many spare parts and magazines and millions of 45 calibre ammunition were stored in the holds of the *East Side*. Back in Ireland, Collins had given considerable thought to the development. By that time only a few people in Ireland knew about the existence of the Thompson sub-machinegun on a strictly need-to-know basis. Collins himself, Tom Hales, O/C in West Cork, Tom Barry, the famous column leader, and Florence O'Donoghue, Head Centre for the Brotherhood in County Cork. In Dublin, only Mulcahy, Chief of Staff and Cathal Brugha, Minister for Defence, were privy to the plans. The master plan had been evolving in Collins's mind in conjunction with O'Donoghue and Hales for several months, based upon their enormous enthusiasm for the activities of Tom Barry's Column in West Cork and the homeric battles he had fought at Kilmichael and Crossbarry. Barry had about a hundred trained, seasoned fighting men in his column, but they were hampered by the lack of arms. They didn't have enough Enfield rifles for everyone, but there were plenty of able volunteers throughout Cork and in the City. O'Donoghue estimated that they could raise 5–8,000 thousand fighting men if they had the equipment for them. Barry's enthusiasm had ignited a flame in Collins's mind and for that reason he had been brought into the plan at an early stage.

The strategic plan was that the ship with the consignment of Thompson guns, would sail into Baltimore Harbour in West Cork, drop anchor, the area would be completely sealed off by Barry's column, and a flotilla of trawlers and fishing boats would empty the cargo off the *East Side*, which would be immediately dispersed amongst the Cork battalions. An intensive training procedure would be adopted immediately and the rest of the plan would fit like clockwork.

The first assault would be made on Bandon, sweeping Percival and the Essex Regiment out of their way and a direct assault made on Cork, with a major uprising of all rebels in the county and all the arms that were being, hopefully, taken from the Auxiliaries and the British Army in Barry's drive, would have sealed the British Army in Cork, putting the City in Barry's hands. The three Cork Brigades would become the vanguard of the Army of Munster, under Liam Lynch, and they would have 20,000 armed rebels on the road to Dublin within a week. The Dublin Brigade would have a replay of Easter Week, as soon as the Army of Munster invested the British at the Curragh.

Barry was confident that his men would have superior fire power, local knowledge, public support and motivation. There would have been a tremendous impact and result from this daring stroke. The Cork IRA would be much better armed than the British at the point where they would first attack the Essex in Bandon, and the news would stun and demoralise the Government in London. It was a daring plan and one which very nearly succeeded. Michael Collins had promised himself a few wild days in Cork, under the Tricolour. But the entire Napoleonic plan hinged upon the 500 Thompson submachine guns. It took little account of British air and naval power, but would have ended in a situation in which the British would have had to make visible preparations for a major European war, which would be – hopefully – impossible of her in the prevailing national and international climate.

One of the important matters to which they gave a lot of attention was the question of training. The volunteers, who had been used to revolvers and Enfield rifles worked by bolt action, would take several hours of intensive training before they could use the new sub-machineguns properly and without waste and each officer in turn would be training several others. They had two United States Officers, Major Dineen and Captain Cronin, who were experienced arms instructors and they would be the first to start the training on Barry's column. Emmet Dalton had joined the General Headquarters staff as Director of Training a short time before. In early June, Dalton was instructed to proceed to Cork and make plans with O'Donoghue and Hales for training camps to be set up. It was expected that the "East Side" would arrive in Baltimore about 27 June.

On 16 June, twelve hours before the *East Side* was due to sail, it was raided by an army of customs men and agents from the U.S. Department of Justice. Five hundred machineguns were discovered and the cargo impounded. It would reappear several years later as the major armament of the G-Division of the F.B.I. and the G-men with their Tommy Guns became forever identified in the public mind with the Prohibition period. As soon as the news broke that the Sinn Féiners had lost 500 Thompson guns, British newspapers claimed the raid as a coup for British Intelligence and speculated that they had had a tip off.

Florence O'Donoghue was also adjutant of Cork No. 1 Brigade and he had received an initial shipment of 30 guns sometime in April of 1921. It was at that time also that Mulcahy had been consulted by Collins and later he had appointed Emmet Dalton as Director of Training. Sean Russell and Liam Mellowes were also involved and on the evening of 24 May, Tom Barry, on a visit to Dublin, was included in the first trial party by Collins, Mulcahy, O'Sullivan and six men from the Squad. Barry was delighted. He felt that the Thompson would be an ideal guerrilla weapon and a column equipped with Thompson machineguns would be a potent force, ideal for short range work and the gun would have the additional virtue of being easy to dismantle, a light hard hitting automatic weapon, easy to conceal with enormous fire power. He looked forward to the day when he could settle accounts with the Essex Regiment, but it was not to be. The members of Collins' Squad and the ASU who had tried out the weapon were euphoric at the prospect of meeting the Black-and-Tans on the streets of Dublin, when they were armed with Thompsons.

The first time the Thompson gun was ever used in anger was in an ambush in Drumcondra on 16 June when two were used in an attack upon a troop train, causing heavy casualties on the British. The episode of the Thompson sub-machineguns and the *East Side* was a deep disappointment to Collins and the Supreme Council of the Brotherhood. Years had been spent and enormous sums of money, and it seemed a simple accident or loose tongue in America had caused all the damage. Collins' gift for detecting traitors, informers and spies, had been directed so far outwards; he had not looked at the General Headquarters staff of the IRA. But the taciturn cocky young Dalton had changed history.

TWELVE

De Valera Returns

On 26 November 1920, Arthur Griffiths, the acting President of the Republic in De Valera's absence in America, was himself arrested, and he promptly nominated Michael Collins as his successor in Office as President. For the next few months, therefore, Collins was Head of the Government, the Official Head as well as being Head of the IRB, and of course, by Fenian tradition, being Head Centre of the Brotherhood, the real head of the whole movement and of the revolutionary Government.

De Valera, watching jealously from afar, grew increasingly disconcerted at the growing public status and political influence of Collins. This was dangerously different from backroom popularity amongst the IRA. Collins was plainly more than just a cut-and-thrust leader of wild lads but was emerging as a politician of statesman-like calibre. It was time for De Valera to return home to defend his fiefdom.

During the same period, Lloyd-Geoge busied himself in mock overtures for a truce, with all kinds of busybodies, while firmly blocking any attempt to make direct contact with the Republican Government. This cat and mouse game, for a while, satisfied the King, to whom he had promised overtures of peace. But on December 10th, the southern counties of Cork, Kerry, Tipperary and Limerick were placed under martial law, with curfew and with the death sentence for the possession of arms and explosives. The next day, a major assault was made upon Cork City after a curfew. The streets were filled with police and troops, and the commercial centre of the City was deliberately set on fire, The Opera House and the City Hall were severely damaged, and two members were shot by the Tans while attempting to put out the fire, and many more were wounded. During this period, of course, the general atmosphere was frightful throughout the country, and in the first 20 days of December, 33 men and boys were murdered or tortured to death in a very brutal fashion by the Tans and Auxiliaries. At the same time, the guerrilla war continued, particularly in the brigade areas covered by the martial law, which had the effect of exposing more troops to attack.

De Valera secretly returned from America on Christmas Day, and began to re-assert his own authority. He was appalled when his first question about the course of the struggle was answered. "Sure, things are going great – The Big Fellow is leading us and we have the Brits on the run". De Valera's grim reply was "We will see who is the Big Fellow now".

As far as the IRB were concerned, De Valera returned under a cloud, following his fratricidal conflict with the organisation in the US, and his various political gaffes there. One of these was his public acceptance of a subordinate position in the Empire, similar to Cuba *vis-à-vis* the United States. This caused a public uproar and was the first public faltering by any Irish leader on a question of the Republic, being keenly observed by the Welsh wizard at Westminster.

Another was when he permitted John Devoy to introduce him to the American public as the "President of the Irish Republic", an office which did not legally exist and to which he had never been elected. This touched a nerve in the members of the Brotherhood as he knew it would, in view of their own venerable oath of loyalty to their Head Centre, Michael Colllins as "in fact as well as by right, the President of the Irish Republic".

There was also the question of the US funds, which should have been returned to the Minster of Finance, Michael Collins, but which were retained in the US under De Valera's personal control for another ten years, although these monies had been subscribed for the prosecution of the Anglo-Irish war. However the general public did not know of these stresses and strains and they rejoiced that "Dev" was back home again.

The Dáil met in secret and De Valera's suggestion was to adopt a resolution to formally accept responsibility for all the activities of the Volunteers who would be regarded, constitutionally, as the Army of the Dáil. He announced this at a press conference, and the repercussions were widespread. A great deal of sympathy, support and understanding then obtained for a further struggle to be carried out by the IRA.

However, there were rumours of differences increasing in intensity, between Collins, the most active GHQ officer, and Brugha, as the Minister for Defence, and very often Richard Mulcahy, who was the Chief of Staff, was unable to keep the peace between them. An idea was floated, which was accepted by Mulcahy, much against Collins's will, that the Army would be reorganised in terms of Divisions. This appeared to have been a disastrous mistake, introducing an element of bureaucracy into a guerrilla struggle, which was proceeding with great success.

Up to this time there had been local companies, local battalions, and in each county, at least one or sometimes two or three brigades, depending on the strength of the population, and each brigade would have it's own Active Service Unit or Flying Column, with a large number of part-time volunteers who would assemble when needed for a particular operation, and would provide intelligence and maintenance services. The system was extremely flexible, to minimise damage and worked perfectly. However, it was decided to merge larger bodies of men together and to adopt a more formal military structure, which, in hindsight, appears to be unsatisfactory and unsuitable for a guerrilla war.

The Divisionalisation scheme sprang from a theory of De Valera's that the war should now be progressed by a series of major pitched battles every month involving about 500 men on each side, which would be regarded by the world's press as more newsworthy than the present guerrilla struggle with random ambushes. The concept was little short of lunacy, and would have swiftly led to the destruction of the IRA, since the British would probably not limit their troops to 500 on any set occasion, but pour in reinforcements and might even use artillery and the planes of the Royal Flying Corps, who had accumulated considerable experience in strafing and bombing villages in the Middle East.

But Collins, Lynch, Barry and the fighting commandants in the field were ignored by De Valera and Brugha. The GHQ Staff were compelled to obey orders from the political Cabinet, and Collins took little satisfaction in reminding the Staff that he had warned of these kinds of developments when it was first proposed that each Volunteer take an Oath of Loyalty to the Dáil and Government.

After a lot of discussion, it was decided that Headquarters would appoint divisional commanders, with the rank of Commandant General, and these would be paid, initially, five pounds per week. A number of divisions were created, fifteen in all. This resulted, in some cases, in bringing the best and most aggressive and active commandants into a bureaucratic network where they had a lot of meetings, discussions, reports and staff work, and some of the most active officers from the Flying Columns, became wrapped up in discussing and talking about the War rather than getting on with the job of fighting it. But the decision was made, and De Valera and the Minister of Defence were extremely insistent that it should carried out and carried out it was, despite a good deal of heartsearching and some very harsh words from the commandants of the most active Units. The political result of this Divisionalisation was that the senior fighting officers were removed somewhat from the direct influence of Collins, and came more within the ambit of the Minster of Defence, Cathal Brugha and indirectly of Eamonn De Valera.

At the initial formation, the first Division, in fact, became the Second Southern Division, comprising of the counties of Kilkenny, Limerick and Tipperary, and the Commander was Earnan O'Malley. He was extremely young, he was only 23 when he commanded the Division, many of his senior officers could have been his grandfather, but he was one of the most aggressive fighting officers in the whole of the IRA. He joined after 1916, and had participated in a number of spectacular gun battles and prison escapes. He was not the most diplomatic at times, but he was an extremely fine officer, possibly the best single fighting officer the movement produced.

The Commandant of the First Southern Division was General Liam Lynch, a popular Corkman and a brilliant Staff Officer. The Third Southern Division with Michael McCormack commanding in the counties of Laois, Offaly and Tipperary. Then a division was formed in the West, the First Western covered Clare and South Galway with Mick Brennan, who was an excellent Commander. Mid-Connaght Second Western Division was General Tom Maguire,

North Connaght was Liam Pilkington of Sligo, a brilliant and hard working officer. The Fourth Western Division had Michael Kilroy in command. The Midland Division comprised of Longford, Leitrim and Westmeath, with Commandant General Sean MacEoin commanding. In the North, the First Northern Division covering Donegal, with four brigades, with Joseph Sweeney. The Second Northern was Tyrone and Derry with four brigades with Charlie Daly commanding. The Third Northern Division with Belfast, Antrim and North Derry with Joseph McKelvey commanding. The Fourth Northern was Armagh and South Down/Louth with three brigades under Commandant Frank Aiken. The Fifth Northern covered Monaghan, Fermanagh and Cavan under Commandant Dan Hogan.

In the East of the country, the First Eastern Division of Kildare was under Commandant Sean Boylan. The Dublin Number One was under Oscar Traynor. South Dublin was under Andy McDonnell and Wicklow was Commandant Joseph Cummins. The Carlow Brigade was commanded by Liam Stack. Of these men, Liam Lynch was to die, as was Joe McKelvey and Charlie Daly of the Second Northern, in the Civil War, and at the hands of their own comrades. Despite all the care of Brugha and DeValera, the majority of the divisional staff officers were members of the Brotherhood, since the IRB had always been the nursery of fighting men, and their quality was recognised.

It took a considerable time, up to six months, before this divisionalisation took place and in the meantime there was a certain easing-off in military activity, despite the chafing by Michael Collins and some other GHQ officers with a more aggressive attitude than the Cabinet itself. At the same time, many members of the Cabinet, were engrossed in staking-out positions for the forthcoming truce talks, which all now realised could not be very long delayed. By this time Lloyd George, who was well informed of the political tension between De Valera and Collins, and the general disorganisation of the IRA in the throes of Divisionalisation, had decided that the time was ripe to dangle a baited hook in the troubled waters. There was a considerable shock in store for the Cabinet when De Valera was arrested in a swoop on 22 June, in Blackrock, fortunately by troops rather than Black-and-Tans, which would inevitably have been fatal.

Lloyd-George's "Man in the Castle", Andy Cope, nearly had a seizure at the news, being more shocked than the Irish Cabinet. By pressurising the GOC, he was able to have De Valera detained in military custody, and using Lloyd-George, succeeded to have him released the next day. It was, of course, of great importance that De Valera, Griffiths and Collins be free to accept the Truce terms. Two days later De Valera received an official letter from Lloyd-George inviting him to attend a conference in London with Craig, the Unionist leader, to explore the possibility of a settlement.

On 27 June 1921, the newspapers announced that there had been an invitation from Lloyd-George to De Valera, to come to London to discuss the possibility of a truce in the war, and the feasibility of a settlement. The text of

Lloyd-George's invitation was as follows:

"From Mr D Lloyd-George to Mr De Valera; June 24th 1921

Sir,

The British Government are deeply anxious that, as far as they can assure it, the King's appeal for reconciliation in Ireland shall not have been made in vain. Rather than allow another opportunity of settlement in Ireland to be cast aside, they felt it incumbent upon them to make a final appeal, in the spirit of the King's words, for a Conference between themselves, and the representatives of Southern and Northern Ireland.

I write, therefore, to convey the following invitation to you, as the chosen leader of the great majority in Southern Ireland, and to Sir James Craig, the premier of Northern Ireland.

(1) That you should attend a conference here in London, in company with Sir James Craig, to explore the possibility of a settlement.
(2) That you should bring with you for the purpose, any colleagues whom you select. The Government will, of course, give a safe-conduct to all who may be chosen to participate in the conference.
(3) We make this invitation with a fervent desire to end the ruinous conflict which has for centuries divided Ireland, and embittered the relations of the peoples of these two islands, who ought to live in neighbourly harmony with each other, and whose co-operation would mean so much, not only to the Empire, but to humanity.

We wish that no endeavour should be lacking on our part to realise the King's prayer, and we ask you to meet us, as we will meet you, in the spirit of conciliation for which His Majesty has appealed.

I am, Sir

Your Obedient Servant,

D. Lloyd George".

De Valera replied as follows:

Sir,

I have received your letter.

I am in consultation with such of the principal representatives of our nation as are present. We most earnestly desire to help in bringing about a lasting peace between the peoples of these two islands., but see no avenue by which it can be reached if you deny Ireland's essential unity, and set aside the principle of national self-determination.

Before replying fully to your letter, I am seeking a conference with certain representatives of the political minority of the country.

Eamon De Valera,

Mansion House, Dublin.

De Valera replied again, in a further letter; July 8, 1921

"Sir,

The desire you express on behalf of the British Government to end the centuries of conflict between the people's of these two Islands, and to establish relations of neighbourly harmony, is the genuine desire of the people of Ireland.

I have consulted with my colleagues, and secured the view of the representatives of the minority of our nation in regard to the invitation you sent me.

In reply, I desire to say that I am ready to meet and discuss with you on what basis such a Conference as that proposed can reasonably hope to achieve the object desired.

I am, Sir,

Faithfully yours

Eamon De Valera

Truce terms were quickly agreed within the following parameters:

On behalf of the British Army is agreed the following:
(1) No incoming troops, RIC, and Auxiliary Police and munitions, and no movements for the military purposes of troops and munitions, except maintenance drafts.
(2) No provocative display of forces, armed or unarmed.
(3) It is understood that all provisions of the Truce apply to the Martial Law area equally with the rest of Ireland.
(4) No pursuit of Irish officers and men, or war material, or military stores.
(5) No secret agents, noting descriptions or movements and no interference with the movements of Irish persons, military or civil, and no attempts to discover the haunts or habits of Irish officers and men.

Note: This supposes the abandonment of curfew restrictions.

(6) No pursuit or observance of lines of communication or connection.

Note: There are details connected with courts martial, motor permits, and ROIR to be agreed later.

On behalf of the Irish Army, it is agreed that:
(a) Attacks on Crown forces and civilians are to cease.
(b) No provocative displays of forces, armed or unarmed.
(c) No interference with the British Government or private property.
(d   To discountenance and prevent any action likely to cause disturbance of the Peace which might necessitate military interference.

The Truce came into effect at 12 noon on 11 July 1921.

THIRTEEN

The Truce

The truce came as a great surprise to the members of the Dáil and the members of the Army fighting in the field, particularly to the hardest pressed and the most active in the martial law area, the First and Second Southern Divisions under Liam Lynch and Earnan O'Malley. There was surprise and resentment amongst the fighting officers in the field who had not been consulted about what was both a military and political decision. "we are winning, everyday getting a little stronger, and the British more defensive. Why not wait a few months longer?" was a common attitude. However, immediately afterwards a new atmosphere permeated the whole country.

There was an enormous sense of relief that the fighting and killing had stopped, together with apprehension for the future. But underlying it was a tremendous pride, a sense of having come through a great testing time, and that the plucky little nation had succeeded, in the end, in forcing the richest and strongest Empire in the world to treat it as an equal.

From the beginning, it was apparent that Lloyd-George and the British Government miscalculated the relative political positions of Collins and De Valera. It was unclear to what extent they understood the dichotomy between the office of President of the Dáil, which was De Valera's official position, and that of President of the IRB, which was recognised by the Brotherhood as that of President of the Irish Republic, which, in effect, was Collins's position, and this unrelieved and unfinalised dichotomy was to cause a great deal of trouble. The British were apparently under the impression that Collins was a more determined and more extreme Republican, and De Valera was relatively moderate. This was largely because of the fact that while De Valera spoke publicly in mild and moderate terms on almost all occasions, he was extremely forthright and hardline in private, because when he was speaking in Cabinet, he was invariably flanked by Cathal Brugha and Austin Stack, both of whom were very single-minded extremist Republicans. DeValera was always keenly observant of the need to protect his flank against Collins, and he had no qualms about misleading Brugha and Stack regarding his real ideas and principles.

A measure of the inordinate influence of Brugha on De Valera is given by a report of the full meeting of the Republican Government to discuss Lloyd George's initial proposals for Truce negotiations, which clearly indicated that there was no possibility of the British agreeing to a Republic.

De Valera had the British letter read out and his draft reply, then asked the members present for their observations. Only Cosgrave, Griffiths and McNeill agreed with De Valera's response. At the end Cathal Brugha made a slashing attack on De Valera, which was meekly accepted. Brugha said "I haven't much to add except to say how glad I am that it has been suggested that we circulate these documents, and consider them fully before we meet again, if for no other reason than to give you and the great masters of English you keep at your elbow an opportunity of extricating us from the morass in which ye have landed us."

"We have done our best" De Valera replied "and I have never undertaken to do more than my best."

Brugha snarled:

"We have proclaimed a Republic in arms, it has been ratified by the votes of the people, and we have sworn an oath to defend it with our lives".

"The oath never conveyed to me any more than to do my best in whatever circumstances arise" pleaded De Valera, as the rest of the Government sat stony faced and embarrassed.

"You have accepted a position of authority and responsibility in the Government of the Republic", Brugha replied, striking the table with his fists, "And you will discharge the duties of that Office as they have been defined. I do not want ever again to hear anything else from you." At this the crestfallen President of the Dail made this humble admission: "I think I can promise, Cathal, that you won't have to complain again".

There are several other instances of the extreme measures and stances which De Valera felt compelled to take, in order to preserve his alliance with Brugha and Stack against Collins in the Cabinet. This was to lead to De Valera to make extreme and extravagant exaggerations in Cabinet and Dáil debates, and adopting postures he privately disbelieved.

On the other hand, Collins frequently, when he was speaking to senior officers and on the rare occasions, when he was speaking to journalists, was conscious of the effect that his words would have as a military leader on the morale of the fighting men in the columns and he spoke in clear and definite terms. But being, probably, more aware of what could be obtained from Britain, he was privately considerably less extreme and more practical.

Collins, from his actual experience of living in England, had a clear sense of the core of English beliefs, in the Monarchy and the Empire, and realised that the Irish might have to compromise on the symbols of these realities. He would accept the reality of a united Ireland, with its own Government and Army, and the freedom to evolve as the people wished. In contrast, De Valera gave much more weight to the symbols of the Republic, himself centrally, than to the necessity of securing the North as part of the nation. Be that as it may, Lloyd-George early on sniffed the possibility of driving a wedge between the two men as the first part of his campaign to create as many fissures as possible in the ranks of Sinn Féin, and he had an early success.

An indication of the general reservations of the fighting men at this time was given by the remarks of Collins, and Tom Barry. Collins is on record as commenting "Once a Truce is agreed and we come out in the open, it is extermination for us if the Truce should fail. We shall be like rabbits coming out from their holes".

Barry's subsequent assessment is revealing:

"The truce went on for six long months, and I feel it was deliberately calculated by the British to drag it out as long as they could. They were used to dealing with subject races, and they knew very well that a long truce is always bad for the weaker force. They knew that our morale and effectiveness were bound to deteriorate over a long period. All the British forces in Ireland and all the other places they were occupying at that time, they were all well housed in barracks, they were paid, dressed and fed. But what was our Guerrilla force going to do in that long six months? They had to live and eat and be clothed, and they might have dependants to look after. No one was paying them. When a man was an active service IRA man, he was able to live in the country with us because the people always looked after us. But this didn't happen during the Truce. He might be the eldest of a family of six or seven, or the son of a labourer or small farmer, and when he went home somebody might be hungry and he would have to get to work. A lot of them just graduated out of the area to look for work elsewhere, they couldn't afford to stay around training and maintaining a state of full readiness. I estimated that by the time the Treaty was signed there was at least a thirty percent loss in our effectiveness, structures and our morale. And this was a carefully calculated policy by the British".

A preliminary meeting with the Irish delegation was called for 12 July to discuss the ground rules for the forthcoming peace convention, and for this meeting the Irish delegation was led by De Valera, with Griffiths, Stack, Barton, Childers and Plunkett, and with Michael Collins deliberately excluded. Collins protested about being excluded in this manner, but could get no satisfaction. The Dáil agreed to the delegation as proposed by De Valera. However, when the delegation went to London, the first meeting were private between De Valera and Lloyd-George, and both sides later issued statements that were not totally corresponding in regard to what transpired. It was the first of many meetings in regard to the forthcoming conference, which Lloyd-George later complained, were extremely frustrating.

He found De Valera almost impossible to pin down and he complained somewhat bitterly that negotiating with De Valera was like trying to pick up mercury with a fork, to which De Valera replied, "Why doesn't he use a spoon?" There was a good deal of pirouetting and official position-taking, but both sides desperately needed and wanted to get into a negotiating position.

But from the very beginning, Lloyd-George made it quite clear that there were two matters that the British would not and could not compromise. One of them was the continued existence of the Northern Government, formed by Sir James Craig under the 1920 Government of Ireland Act, which had been invested by his Majesty King George V. The other was the fact that whatever the final settlement would be, it would have to contain an Irish declaration of loyalty to the Commonwealth and to the Crown. Other than that they were prepared to negotiate all kinds of concessions regarding trade and the internal Government of Southern Ireland as a self governing dominion. And they would seek Irish concessions themselves regarding recruitment for the armed forces, the use of the various ports, and a great deal of other matters which, no doubt, the Irish would find extremely irksome, but which could be negotiated away.

De Valera came up against this brick wall of obstinacy in the stately minuet which set out the groundrules upon which the final peace conference would be held, and he could not agree upon the terms. Finally he said to Lloyd-George,

> "You have given me an impossible task. I am the President of the Republic, the living symbol of the Republic. I cannot possibly come here to give away that Republic"

Lloyd-George, seeing his opportunity, replied:

> "Why should you come. Why don't you send someone else?"

By the time this was done, two months had already been wasted.

Lloyd-George's final response to De Valera's attempt to achieve recognition laid the matter very clearly. "Could we therefore send you herewith a fresh invitation to a conference in London on October 11th, where we can meet your delegates as spokesmen of the people who they represent, in a view to ascertaining how the association of Ireland with the community of nations known as the British Empire, may best be reconciled with the Irish national aspirations."

It was probably the most important communication between the two leaders, and quite certainly, in retrospect with the wisdom that hindsight gives, it was clear that the Irish should not have accepted that invitation for that conference on those grounds. There was no need to go to London to say No! Collins later himself said that:

> "The communication of September 29th from Lloyd-George made it clear that they were going into a conference, not on the recognition of the Irish Republic, but if we all stood on the recognition of the Republic as a prelude to any conference, we could have easily said so, and there would have been no conference. It was the acceptance of the invitation which formed the first compromise."

Robert Barton, a member of the Cabinet, who took part in the final conference with Collins, agreed with this assessment, and he said:

> "In these preliminaries the English refused to recognise us as acting on behalf of the Irish Republic, and the fact that we agreed to negotiate on any other basis at all, was possibly, the primary cause of our downfall. Certainly, it was the first milestone on the road to disaster."

However, the administration of the Dáil, the Republican Cabinet, decided to accept the invitation, and thereby made compromise inevitable. On 20 August 1921, there was a long and argumentative meeting of the Cabinet, about who should go to London for the continuation of the peace process. De Valera, who now knew what was possible, was quite determined that he would not lead the Irish delegation towards the inevitable compromise. He would stay in Dublin and he would send the one man who was most dangerous to any compromise to London to make that compromise. He proposed that Collins and Griffiths be joint leaders. In violent argument in Cabinet, Collins declared that he was a soldier, not a politician, he did not have the knowledge or experience, and he resisted bitterly what he realised quite well was a crown of thorns. He was adamant that De Valera, the most experienced politician, as the Leader and the President, should lead the Irish delegation.

But Machiavelli won the argument in the Cabinet and Collins, a soldier, carrying out an impossible order, returned again to the London where he had grown up and flourished, and to his personal Golgotha.

FOURTEEN

Minuet in London

Negotiations opened between representatives of the two countries on Tuesday, 11 October 1921. As the delegation arrived at Downing Street, there was a crowd of men, women and children kneeling in prayer across the street. The Irish had turned out in strength, singing hymns, reciting the Rosary and pouring blessings on the undertaking. There were flags and banners and much jostling and shouting.

Inside Downing Street, in the conference hall, the delegates were formally greeted by Lloyd-George at the door of the conference room. He then escorted them to their side of the large green baize table, across which he introduced them to their opposite numbers on the British side. This was a rather cunning move by the Welsh Warlock. It meant that the delegation would not be required to shake hands with each other, which might have caused some concern amongst the upper ranks of the Tory Party in Britain. But it also meant the De Valera's official credentials need not be presented, and, since the question of recognition of the Irish Republic would be explicit in their acceptance, this was an early British triumph. The documents which the Irish team carried remained as an interesting souvenir. These had been put together with much thought by President De Valera, and read,

> "TO WHOM ALL THESE PRESENTS COME, GREETINGS
>
> In virtue of the authority vested in me by Dáil Éireann, I hereby appoint:
>
> Arthur Griffiths, TD Chairman and Minister for Foreign Affairs.
> Michael Collins, TD Minister of Finance.
> Robert Barton, TD Minister of Economic Affairs.
> Eamonn J. Duggan, TD
> George Gavan Duffy, TD
>
> as Envoys Plenipotentiary from the Elected Government of The REPUBLIC OF IRELAND to negotiate and conclude of behalf of Ireland with the representatives of His Britannic Majesty, George V, a Treaty or Treaties of settlement, Association and Accommodation between Ireland and the community of nations known as the British Commonwealth.
>
> IN WITNESS WHEREOF I hereunto subscribe my name as President."

The Irish delegation was a curious choice to negotiate a fruitful Peace for a small nation victorious in a guerrilla war. Griffiths and Collins had considerable political gifts and grasp of events, but Griffiths certainly lacked either confidence in Irish ability to win complete separation from the Empire, or even the desirability of such, and was inwardly prepared to compromise on the question of Ulster and the Crown and Empire before he went to London.

Collins had pride and confidence, tempered with a streak of realism and a sense of proportion. He would certainly extract as much as possible from the circumstances, more so than any other man, but he realised the necessity to compromise on the central themes of the English semi-feudal concepts of the King and Empire. He was prepared to go to war again on the unity of the Republic, even offering the Northern Unionists a devolved federal government in the six counties, but he realised the weakening of the Republican position during the periods of Truce and Treaty negotiations. The other three plenipotentiaries were makeweights, not representing the deposit of talent and political skill available in Dáil Éireann at the time.

Duggan was a lawyer, almost a caricature of obeisance as appears in Tom Barry's acid account of his behaviour as Chief Liaison Officer for all Ireland, knowing nothing of the IRA but representing them to General Macready, and practically licking Macready's boots. Barton was an ex-British Army officer, and a Protestant landowner in Co Wicklow, a very honest and conscientious gentleman but not noted for mental agility and comprehension. Gavan Duffy, another lawyer, scion of a famous family , a good sound man, but not in the same class as the many capable and experienced British negotiators.

Of the five plenipotentaries, only Collins was a member of the Brotherhood. It is a fair conclusion that De Valera, skilled in intrigue as he was, ensured the result, knowing that the British would never concede a Republic and knowing also that failure on this point would destroy the one man he feared in all the Dáil.

Erskine Childers, cousin of Robert Barton, and Howth gun-runner in his yacht, *Asgard*, was Chief Secretary to the delegation, and was much more effective than most of the plenipotentaries. Curiously, his assistants included John Charteris, his cover now blown, and acting partly as legal advisor to Collins, in which capacity he drafted the compromise Oath of Loyalty to the King, which was accepted by the Council of the IRB, he also doubled as Collin's ADC in the various arms importations which continued all during the Treaty negotiations. Another Brother, young Sean MacBride also doubled as the Delegation official Courier to the Dublin Government, and Collins personal courier to the IRB executive, and occasionally handled urgent tasks connected with the international aspects of gun running. During all the negotiations the Brotherhood were fully informed of progress and kept alive a keen and constructive interest in development.

By not having to accept the Irish credentials and the explicit recognition which acceptance would imply, Lloyd-George neatly removed a potent weapon from the hands of the Irish delegation. Then began the slow, stately minuet in London between the two delegations, of which the British was larger, much more experienced and sophisticated, and much more competent at the task before them.

The British team consisted of David Lloyd-George, the Premier, Lord Birkenhead, Austin Chamberlain and Winston Churchill. Alongside them his advisors were Sir Gordon Hewett, the Attorney General, Sir Lamington Worthington Evans, Conservative Secretary for War and Sir Henry Greenwood, Secretary for Ireland. Outside the chamber, two of Lloyd-George's most brilliant civil servants, Lionel Curtis and Tom Jones, and beyond them again, all the resources of the Empire. Andy Cope was constantly on hand, and hovering around the Irish delegation's headquarters was the sombre and acid figure of Tim Healy. The Irish team were withdrawn and somewhat morose when they realised the full extent of the odds against them. But Collins made a determined effort and a successful effort to establish a rapport with his enemies, on the basis that he was not taking anything personal, and he would fight for the Republic as best they could, but in the middle of the battle, he would reach out his hand to them in friendship. His legendary personal magnetism was here facing its greatest test, and he made a deep and favourable impression on several of his bitterest enemies, who had previously regarded him as a bandit and anarchist.

He was particularly successful in achieving a friendly personal relationship with Lord Birkenhead, who would have been poles apart from him in background. He never got on friendly terms with Lloyd-George, perhaps because they were both Celts. Birkenhead had a very long knowledge and experience of Irish politics, as Galloper Smith, a young lawyer and supporter of Carson during the Home Rule agitations. Later within Treaty debates in the House of Lords, he indicated that he had been won over by Collins's personality and his persuasive arguments, and in fact, was an advocate of Collins's policies and of the Treaty against Carson, who was by now, embittered and morose, having been sidelined into the backwater of the Lords and his hands lifted rudely from the levers of power.

Carson himself commented on the whole sordid story of his Orange years. In an outburst of bitterness in the House, he said:

> "I was in earnest. I was not playing politics. What a fool I was. I was only a puppet, and so was Ulster, and so was Ireland in the political game that was to get the Conservative Party into power."

They were now grasping with the great historical problems that were now pressing. In the end, Churchill played a prominent part in getting the Anglo-Irish Treaty through the House. There was definitely a strong chemistry between Collins and Churchill, which sprang from a clear recognition of their mutual political antagonism and their mutual respect as people.

The Irish delegation divided and Griffiths and what might be called the more sober and staid members were staying in Hans Place, but Collins and the younger officers who had come with him were staying in Cadogan Gardens, in a house which has become notorious for rumbustious and noisy folics. Throughout each morning the delegation would meet to discuss the slow, tortuous edging towards each other of the two nations, afternoons the delegation would retire to their individual offices and discuss what had been gone over in the morning and make preparations for the next day. But in the evenings, matters changed considerably.

The principle catalyst in this change was Lady Hazel Lavery, who was then one of London's most glamorous hostesses. A bizarre note was struck during the long negotiations, when Kevin O'Higgins, who was Minister for Home Affairs at home, came to London for his wedding with Birdie Cole, a teacher from Waterford. O'Higgins' best man was Rory O'Connor, and their warm friendship was to have an extraordinary ending.

Even though he was newly married and on his honeymoon, O'Higgins was captivated by the extraordinary personality of Lady Hazel, and a relationship began which was to last for several years, in the course of which, O'Higgins wrote, what Shane Leslie called, some pathetic poems, because, of course, Hazel had shown these things around. Shane Leslie also wrote a coded commentary on three well known portraits painted by Sir John Lavery, of Collins, Dennison Ross and a classical allegory of Hazel as Leda and the Swan. The latter picture depicted Lady Hazel as Leda, with the great bird between her parted thighs.

> "What feathered denizen of the sea or hills, what proud plumed lover from the mountain or the lake did Lavery suspect when he painted that flowing fluttering trembling view of your surprised and passionate beauty? . . . or was it some amorous flamingo who broke through his bars at the Zoological Gardens or some dreadful nighthawk who clawed and dropped you ere he could carry you to his eyrie or was it some fierce 'wild goose' of Ireland that passed crying in the night."

Shane Leslie, who was a cousin of Churchill's and had been one of Hazel's lovers himself, has tended to exaggerate her influence in bringing about the Treaty, and he perhaps believed too readily her accounts of her amours with Collins. But there was no doubt that from her salon, which was her house and studio, as he said himself, Hazel set out to inveigle the English and Irish Statesmen from the summits to descend to know each other personally as well as politically. Many such as Winston Churchill, Lord Birkenhead, Michael Collins and Arthur Griffiths had reason to remember the luxurious mansion of the Laverys at No. 5, Cromwell Place. The mixture of sex and statesmanship may not have been harmful in another context, but in Michael Collin's perilous position, it was foolish. It was, after all, a traditional weapon of the Empire, used with success in the past.

Although this socialising, "sleeping with the enemy", could have been fairly harmless, it did not lose anything in the telling, and news was getting back to Longford, and indeed, Kitty Kiernan wrote a letter to Collins in which she expressed a certain amount of anxiety about a glamorous English society hostess who was reputed to have offered a thousand pounds to spend just one gorgeous night with Michael Collins. Collins brushed this matter off. There was little doubt that in certain sections of the English establishment women regarded the strange delegation of "wild Irishmen" not only to be looked at and gaped at, but possibly to be sampled as well, and this would appear to have been a long distance from the mores of West Cork.

A North Belfast Unionist MP, H. Montgomery Hyde, wrote later in his book *The Londonderrys* that Collins had a relationship with Lady Edith Londonderry, which is rather more difficult to accept. Lord Londonderry, Charles Stewart, Henry Vane Tempest Stewart, Seventh Marquess of Londonderry, was a direct descendant of Lord Castlereagh, the original Robert Stewart, the father of the Act of Union and the author of much of the bloodletting during the 1798 rebellion. Shelly's description of him cannot be bettered.

"I met Death upon the way – He wore a mask like Castlereagh
Seven Bloodhounds followed him and they were tall and fierce and grim"

The Londonderrys were the core of the Unionist aristocracy, and the present Lord Londonderry was, in fact, slightly more liberal than normal, but had been one of the founders and promoters of the original Unionist Covenant, which many had signed literally in their own blood.

Lady Londonderry was well known from her most luxurious mansion in London, Londonderry House in Park Lane, and she was the mistress of a celebrated social grouping called "The Ark", which included amongst it's membership the Duke of York, who later became King George VI, the Prince of Wales, who later became, briefly, King and then Duke of Windsor, and the Duke of Gloucester, together with, of course, Carson, Balfour, Hailsham, Ramsey McDonald, Churchill, and many literary figures. It would appear from Londonderry's own reminiscences that he was strongly impressed when he met Collins and was won over after a few hours. Not indeed at Collins's politics, which would have struck at the roots of his family fortune, but certainly Collins's personality. Lord Londonderry was well aware of his wife's sexual frolics with Collins, and a contemporary remarked, probably with malice towards both, "Collins is not the first Irishman to be destroyed by a rampant prick – and he won't be the last." His wife, Lady Edith, was probably the second most beautiful society woman in London, Lady Hazel claiming to be the first. This was probably the origin of the story of the society woman who wanted to sleep with Collins. The mixture of decadent sex and aristocracy was one which Collins should have avoided like the plague.

Shane Leslie hints in his book of an incident involving Collins, Lady Londonderry and Churchill, an incongruous menage a trois. This may have happened at Sir Philip Sassoon's house at Port Lympne, where Churchill was down for a weekend, painting and Collins and Edith Londonderry were also guests. There exists a note written from the Lavery's house, in which Collins appears to have expressed himself to Lady Edith in extremely incautious and compromising terms;

> "Forgive me. I bitterly regret my outburst at L. You are very kind to arrange the meeting and I am very well aware that I was miserably minded to listen to W. Churchill.
>
> It is very well to tell me as you do that he has no 'interest' in you. But how can you expect me to believe that, feeling as you know very well how I feel. So you must forgive my bitterness, and try to imagine what it means to be a man like myself entirely self-made, self-educated, without background and trying to cope with a man like Lord L., a man who has every advantage I lack. . . .
>
> I feel savage and unhappy, and so I blame you for a situation for which I alone am to blame, but I contrast myself with my uncouthness, and his distinction, my rough speech and his unconscious breeding, and the worst of it is I like and admire him, and feel he is brave and honest.
>
> On one point alone I believe myself his superior."

One wonders what followed that night that Collins apparently spent in Lady Edith's arms, and it was apocryphically reported that while they were making love, Collins started to chuckle. Edith said, "Michael, what are you laughing at?" to which he is alleged to have retorted, "In West Cork, we would call this the aristocratic embrace." He felt her stiffen under him and he realised that she was not amused. He related the tale to a shocked O'Reilly, who could not keep it to himself. But this was all dangerous dabbling, and was not what he had been sent to London to do. While the rumours abounded, and none lost in the telling eventually when he got back to Ireland, the files in Lloyd-George's desk got thicker and more compromising.

In the midst of all this, between the socialising and the diplomatic conferences each day, Collins still continued to play the third hand, meeting frequently with members of the IRB, occasionally sending Sean MacBride on journeys on the Continent connected with the importation of arms. At the back of his mind there was always the strong possibility that the British, in the end, might produce unacceptable terms and that the fight might have to be resumed again.

He listened intently to the warnings of John Charteris, who played an extraordinary part in these dramatic events. At this stage, the British had not finally made up their minds about Charteris, and were unsure of his exact position and loyalties, which probably saved his life, but some members of MI6 were brooding about revenge for Bloody Sunday. On the obverse side, there was a direct channel from the Irish delegation, and their inmost thoughts and strategies, from Emmet Dalton, who was a military adviser to the Delegation, and from Tim Healy, who was providentially in London for most of the negotiations.

An element of farce intruded on these sombre intrigues, in the security arrangements. Col. Broy, Collin's chief agent in the Castle, came over to London, "blowing his cover" to take charge of security arrangements and act as a bodyguard to Collins: also Neligan the second most important Collins source in the Castle, was sent over by the Castle administration to spy on the Irish delegation from a distance, and report any dubious meetings!

But Lloyd George's real spies monitored every move of Collins, and noted the details of every imprudent assignation, and every incident of internal disagreement in the Irish delegation.

FIFTEEN

The Crucible

From the beginning of the negotiations, Michael Collins and Arthur Griffith had reached a tacit understanding between themselves. Griffith was the titular leader of the negotiation team, and would be regarded as such by the British; Collins was, in fact, the actual leader in the discussions. But they contrived very well to keep this from the British for a considerable part of the negotiations.

On the British side, a somewhat similar situation existed, but the Irish were quick to catch on, to realise the balance of power. Lloyd-George was the Premier, and as such was the Chairman of the Cabinet Committee, which was conducting the negotiations. But there was no doubt that the strongest figure and the one with the deepest roots in the Tory *[Lloyd-George was a Liberal]* Party, whose support would have been necessary, was Winston Churchill, the archetypal representative of British Imperialism, with a history going back to the first Duke of Marlborough. Churchill had many relatives with Irish connections, including Sir Shane Leslie, who has written a lot of informative detail about that period.

It says much for the intuition of both sides that a tremendous amount of the actual work on the treaty took place in private, not at plenary sessions, but at private exploratory talks, of which there were very many between Michael Collins and Winston Churchill. By the end of the long period of negotiations, they were on civilised and understanding terms to each other. They had not accepted the same viewpoint, but they did have a tacit agreement as to how the national disagreements would be thrashed out in the years to come.

On the staff side, the secretaries and senior people rapidly became delineated. On the Irish side, Childers, who had had a colourful career, as the author of the *Riddle of the Sands*, as a officer in British Naval Intelligence during the War, and earlier, as the Captain of the *Asgard* which brought the guns to Howth. He was to die very tragically, as a result of his devotion and his tenacity and the passions aroused during the Civil War, and his son, also Erskine Childers, was later to become President of Ireland. There were a number of other people in the Irish staff, Dermot O'Hegarty and Fionan Lynch and John Charteris. Charteris played an extremely devious and important part in Collins' life, and was quite important in the negotiations. The oath they took as boys in West Cork had changed both their lives.

Charteris joined British Intelligence and played a key role on security duties for the armaments industry. He also attained the confidence of some Sinn Féin leaders, particularly Griffith, writing for various Sinn Fein journals under a pseudonym from 1917, and he was probably one of the first of the many celebrated double or treble agents, of which the 20th century has given us so many dramatic examples. Charteris had married a girl from Piedmont, who was an excellent journalist, and had worked for Sinn Féin under Sean T. O'Kelly in France at the Peace Conference. But for more than four years before the conference itself, Charteris had been a frequent associate of Collins and had carried out many extremely difficult, important and dangerous tasks on behalf of the Army Executive. Almost certainly, his true and final loyalty was to Michael Collins and the Republic.

The British staff included Tom Jones and Lionel Curtis and, of course, Andy Cope, Lloyd-George's personal agent in Ireland, was almost always on hand and acted as go-between Lloyd-George and Griffith and Collins, with both of whom he had established a warm relationship. It is ironic to note that Childers and Curtis had both been at the same school, Haileybury, and both of them had fought in the Boer War on the British side.

From the beginning, Collins and Griffith had decided that the Irish strategy would be centred upon the question of Ulster, that they would be prepared to yield slowly, as little as possible, with dogged defence all the way, but prepared to yield nevertheless, on other peripheral questions; the King's role, the relationship to the Commonwealth, and other matters the British were determined to write into the Treaty. Collins and Griffith both, were quite determined that the final outcome would have to be a single unitary state in Ireland, and there was no question of Ulster, then constituted as six counties, remaining out. There was a feeling that in permitting its temporary administration to go into a full and permanent government, excluded from the rest of the country, a disaster would ensue.

They proceeded on this general line of negotiation. Griffith expounded the Irish claim in a masterly fashion, and focused entirely on the question of Ulster and the relationship of Ulster to the rest of Ireland, while giving the relationship of Ireland to the Crown only a cursory notice. There were several plenary sessions of the negotiations in October. Collins certainly realised that at the far end of tunnel, Dominion status was the only possibility and that the Empire would never concede to the Republic, and certainly, never, never, never concede to a Republic of 32 counties. Collins, then in discussion with Griffith, began to prepare a second line of defence, where at all costs, there must be a united Ireland, and that the relationship that such a united country would have with the Empire, would have to be capable of development in the years to come. As the logical consequence of that policy, Griffith struggled successfully during all the time that remained to prevent the talks from breaking down and he was determined to go back to Dublin with some agreement.

By the end of October, the British decided to break up the major plenary sessions in to a number of sub-conferences of working groups. There were obvious dangers in this, and it was given the worst possible construction by the Cabinet in Dublin. For many years it was thought that this was a cunning British ploy to divide and conquer and it was only long after Tom Jones' diaries were published that it was realised that it was, in fact, Griffith and Collins who proposed this as a method of defusing the major arguments, breaking it down and in each case, reducing the size of the problem to soluble modules. In view of the disparity in military strength between the two sides, it was a very sensible proposal, provided that the men in each of the working groups were extremely keen-minded, quite extraordinarily tenacious in holding firm to the core instructions of the respective Cabinets.

From quite early on in the negotiations there was an obvious strong difference of opinion between the negotiators in London and members of Cabinet back in Dublin. Griffith kept the Cabinet informed of each meeting, but there was not a reciprocal transfer of information from Dublin back to the delegates. From the first major report that Griffith sent back, he stressed the significance that the British people and Government attached to the Crown as an essential part of the Empire. In Griffith's words:

> "They press me to say that I would accept the Crown, provided we came to other agreements. It was everything that they wanted to assure themselves against the diehards on the Tory backbenches. I told them I had no authority, but if we came to agreement on all other points, I would recommend some association with the Crown. I told them that this was the only possibility of Ireland having any association with the Crown. There is in an exchange for essential National unity, a concession on Ulster. The British always fell back upon the impossibility of any peace except on acceptance of the Crown."

De Valera was certainly well aware of this core of British belief, but he ignored it entirely in his formal reply to the delegation on this point. The first paragraph of his reply was:

> "We are all here at one, that there will be no question of our asking the Irish people to enter any agreement which would make them subject to the British King. If War is the alternative, we can only face it, and I think that the sooner the other side is made to realise it, the better."

This was extraordinary sabre-rattling on the part the weakest side in the discussions. The Irish delegation were in a fury when this letter was given to them, and Collins, in particular, stormed and raged and insisted that they would come back home to Dublin. Griffith also threatened to go home, unless the delegation's hands were left free. All the delegates signed a letter of protest to De Valera, Collins rather reluctantly, because the letter to De Valera suggested that he would come over without publicity, which Collins realised was quite an impossibility. Eventually Collins, on Griffith's insistence, signed and the letter was sent. The letter of protest was sent back to the Republican Cabinet, but Collins still threatened to all the delegates, knowing quite well that it would get back to De Valera, that he was on the point of returning to Dublin and to go and join a Flying Column in Cork as an ordinary Volunteer for the war that was to come at De Valera's insistence.

The Cabinet realised that they had gone too far when they got the protest letter from the delegation and they sent a reply which in essence was back-tracking.

> "There was no question of tying the hands of the plenipotentiaries be-yond the extent to which they were tied by their original instructions. Of course, the Cabinet decision cannot be withdrawn or varied except by the Cabinet as a whole. The delegation must understand these memo-randa of mine, except that I explicitly state otherwise, are nothing more than to keep you in touch with the views of the Cabinet here on the various points as they arise. I think it most important that you be kept aware of these views and when the delegation returns there will have to be the question of a Cabinet decision as a policy."

This was the beginning of a persistent campaign, which has been helped by many revisionist pseudo-historians, to the effect that the Irish delegation in London acted as a law unto themselves, without consulting the Dáil or the Government. This is not borne out by the facts, but the campaign has served to foist the blame for many subsequent tragedies onto Collins and Griffith.

The growth of mutual distrust between Collins and De Valera was not helped by actions being taken by De Valera and Brugha as Minister of De-fence, to persuade the Dáil to agree to a new scheme of offering all the officers fresh commissions, subject to the officers taking a second oath of loyalty to the Dáil. This was a proposal for a new army and caused a tremendous amount of confusion and anger amongst the ranks of the fighting officers who had brought the fight to such a successful conclusion so far. They were particularly angered and disturbed that this proposal was taken while Collins was in London and immersed in the discussions in trying to bring about a treaty with the ancient enemy. On hearing of the proposal, Collins wrote to General Mulcahy on 23 November:

> "I heard from Mr Griffith that the new Cabinet has been summoned for 25th to meet the GHQ Staff of the old Army. It reminds me of Napo-leon. The members of Cabinet, at present in London, have been asked to be present. I think we ought to have a meeting with the GHQ staff very early on Friday morning, before the Cabinet meeting. I also suggest that we should have associates at that meeting, directors of the staff, who have given a certain time in the old Army, directors who really did operate, not nominal directors. People like Staines etc, who have a great knowledge of the staff and know what went on in the days when it was hard work to organise and to run the old Army. In pledge, I send you a

copy of a letter that was written yesterday by Mr. Griffith, giving details of Lloyd-George's and Birkenhead's reception of the Irish proposal for the Treaty."

Collins and Griffith went back to Dublin on the train and boat, and discussed the matter at the Cabinet meeting. Mulcahy, who also had read Machiavelli, proposed to the Cabinet that before the old Army was disbanded, that GHQ staff should be brought in and thanked for their past services and told about the new organisational plan. This ceremony took place after Collins and Griffith had explained to the Cabinet in Dublin what was the current state of the negotiations in London and also after Collins had met with the Council of the IRB, who promptly briefed the officers on the GHQ staff. Collins and Griffith then went back on the boat from Dun Laoghaire and were actually on the train to London when De Valera called in the officers to the Cabinet.

The GHQ staff officers unanimously turned down the "New Army" proposal. They were a "Band of Brothers" and no change was necessary. Eoin O'Duffy said that he found the proposals personally insulting. De Valera realised that although Collins might be hundreds of miles away on a train to London, his presence was in the Cabinet, and in the loyalty and the hearts and minds of the staff officers. The President interrupted O'Duffy and it is reported that he rose very excitedly, pushed the table in front of him away, and half screaming, half shouting, said "you may mutiny if you like, but Ireland will give me another army" and he promptly dismissed them from the Cabinet room. Brugha and Stack calmed him down, and he realised that it would be madness to attempt to withdraw the army in the middle of the negotiations, and build a new one. The idea of establishing a new army was quietly dropped but more damage had been done to the relationships between the delegates in London and the others in the Cabinet back in Dublin.

The rift between Collins and De Valera was now out in the open, and so far, it had little to do with politics or the Treaty terms, but much more to do with the fatal claim of the Brotherhood that their secret President was also the invisible President of the Irish Republic.

Despite the oft-repeated lies that the delegation did not consult the Cabinet before signing the Treaty, they actually travelled to Dublin for a Cabinet meeting the previous weekend, Griffith on 2 December and Collins on the 3rd, exhausted and in ill-humour. The journey on the mailboat from Holyhead was greatly delayed by a collision with an Arklow vessel, which cost two lives. Collins arrived in Dun Laoghaire, barely an hour before the vital Cabinet meeting, exhausted, sleepless and in low spirits.

Collins had first to meet the Brotherhood Secretary, O'Muirthuile, and brief the Council on the latest developments. This was a very hurried meeting, on Dun Laoghaire Pier, and the Council remained in session during the Cabinet meeting, and O'Muirthuile again met Collins during a lunch break. At this meeting he confirmed to Collins that the IRB would, reluctantly, accept the form of the Oath, drafted by Charteris, and he gave a warm endorsement to the efforts of the team in London. Collins returned to the Cabinet in better spirits.

There then ensued an unpleasant, inconclusive meeting, lasting all day, with no clear directions being given to the plenipotentiaries. There was much hair-splitting, and De Valera as chairman, repeatedly refused to take a vote on the issues. The room was crowded, with people who were not all members of the Cabinet, but including the secretaries and advisers, Charteris, Dalton and Childers, who spoke for and against the questions, but no proper record or minutes were taken of this crucial meeting. Collins was very largely silent during the futile discussions, and it seems that he had little respect for the Cabinet proceedings. He did state, baldly, that the non-acceptance of the proposed Treaty terms would be a gamble with peace or war, and England could arrange war within a week. He would hold the line on Ulster, but it might be necessary to concede on other peripheral matters. There was no definite instructions from this meeting, despite the fact that the Irish delegation were to meet the British team within two days for a final decision.

The British soon became aware of the extraordinary fact that the major part of the discussions and wrangling centred around the precise form of the Oath to the Head of the Commonwealth, and little to the brutal fact that the country was being partitioned and the Irish population in most of Ulster would be left supine and helpless at the feet of their bitterest enemies. At the end of that mournful, fruitless day, Collins and Griffith left to join the mailboat at Dun Laoghaire, for an unpleasant journey back to London. The Supreme Council of the IRB considered the state of the negotiation, Collins being absent at the indeterminate Cabinet meeting. However the IRB gave him clear and definite instructions, which were in line with his own opinion. O'Muirthuile met him at Dun Laoghaire on his way to the mailboat, and the two walked to the East Pier as the instructions of the Council were discussed.

Three obstacles remained to a settlement. First, the Oath of direct Allegiance to the British King, second the proposal for Ireland's coastal defence, and thirdly and most important, the proposals for partition and a Unionist government in the North.

The Council had agreed to accept the amended Oath, proposed by John Charteris, in terms suggested by Crompton Llewellyn Davies. They left the question of coastal defence to the discretion of the plenipotentiaries to be compromised on if necessary, and they rejected partition absolutely. Collins agreed that he would pursue these instructions to the best of his ability, and break the negotiations on the question of Ulster, if it came to that. He then boarded the mailboat for London and the final confrontation with the British delegation.

SIXTEEN

Blackmail

On the morning of the 4 December, Collins had a private discussion with Lloyd-George, following the lengthy meetings between Griffith and Andy Cope the previous day. Collins outlined the Irish delegation's difficulties, principally on Ulster, but also on certain items of trade, defence and the Oath of Loyalty. At the end of that meeting, the two countries were as close as they could have ever been, before or since, to understanding and agreement. Lloyd-George had been impressed by Andy Cope's reports and those his own secretary, Tom Jones. Both he and Collins were ready to make necessary concessions to each other's view point. Collins stated that he would accept the opening clause of the proposed treaty maintaining the Irish Free State within the Commonwealth, and the other items, with the exception of Ulster, were minor matters which could be settled. But on the question of Ulster, Collins was totally and absolutely obdurate. He said that it would be the responsibility of the British Government to ensure that Sir James Craig and the Unionists would accept the fundamental unity of Ireland within the Commonwealth, and that he would guarantee that the Irish Dáil and the Republican Movement would accept this compromise. Lloyd-George agreed to telegraph Craig with this final request.

On the afternoon of the same day, Collins went back to Downing Street with Griffith and Barton and again went over the four points that he had mentioned to Lloyd-George, Chamberlain, Birkenhead and Churchill. It was agreed by all present that the only really difficult final disagreement was on the question of Ulster, and the overall unity of the country within the Commonwealth. Collins and Griffith both indicated that they were prepared to accept, or at least, discuss arrangements for devolved local government within the area claimed by the Unionists under the Government of Ireland Act 1920. This was a hint of a federal or confederal compromise, but it was stillborn.

Griffith cherished a previous memorandum by Lloyd-George, in which he had stated that, if Ulster did not accept the principle of an All-Ireland Parliament, the British would create one anyway, and would allow Ulster to remain subject to the Imperial power and of the Reserved Services in such an event, but the boundary of the reserved area would be revised by a boundary commission and would not correspond to the nine counties of Ulster. Griffith hoped that this area would be only two and one half counties. The Boundary Commission became a fatal will-o-the wisp that lured the Irish delegation into concessions without firm guarantees that weakened the entire Irish position. The concept of local autonomy, of decisions by townlands and district electoral areas were freely tossed around by the British, and it was clear to the Irish that, in the event that there was an honest Boundary Commission, the Unionist State would comprise about two-and-a half counties, or three at most. It was also clear to the Unionists, who were apprised daily of all the transactions.

Collins was of the opinion that the Boundary Commission proposal did not, in any way, help to clear up the confusion. He was firmly opposed to a re-partition, leaving the problem still unresolved, and strove for acceptance of the concept of a unitary state, with a parliament in Dublin, to which any assembly in the North, whatever the extent of its territory, would be a federal or confederal constituent, and to achieve this end, he was quite prepared to accept membership of the Commonwealth, and recognition of the King as titular Head. But since Lloyd George had proffered the concession, Collins grasped it firmly and included it as a key element in his future Northern Policy. But even on the Boundary Commission, Perfidious Albion could not resist welshing.

A major step forward at this meeting was the draft that Collins had presented on a new oath. The wording of the "British Commonwealth" was substituted for the "Empire" and there were seven other changes. The new oath had, in fact, been largely drafted by the Supreme Council of the IRB who had considered it at an early stage and had left it to three of their more prominent members, who were also GHQ Officers, to prepare a more satisfactory alternative. The new oath introduced allegiance to the Irish Free State in the first instance and the King in the subordinate clause. The British agreed to the reform of the oath, that in the final analysis had been decided by the Supreme Council of the IRB. The original wording for this oath had been drafted by John Charteris, helped greatly by private conversations with Crompton Llewellyn-Davies, and submitted through Collins to the Supreme Council.

The final sub-conference on the afternoon of 5 December, skimmed rapidly over the questions of Irish Free State military defence, but they balked briefly at the restriction of the Irish Naval Service. Churchill was adamant that if an Irish navy were included in the treaty, it would never get through parliament. The British people believed that the Irish ships could be used against them in a time of war. Both sides confirmed agreement that the British Navy would continue to operate facilities in Cork Harbour, Bantry Bay, and Lough Swilly.

It seemed as if the conference was now speeding to an amicable conclusion. They agreed that Ireland would take a major share of her own coastal defence and provision was made in the draft treaty for a review at the end of five years. Collins then took up the vexed question of trade and the British conceded full fiscal autonomy. Lloyd-George informally agreed that there would be freedom on both sides to impose any trade tariffs they wished.

The sub-conference then went back to the thorny question of Ulster. No reply had come from Craig and the Unionists at that time. Griffith indicated that he, personally, would sign the treaty, whether Craig accepted the principle of unity or not. This completely undermined the political position his fellow delegates presented. They were thunderstruck and it was clear that Griffith had not told anyone else of his secret agreement, which he had most foolishly written in a letter to Lloyd-George who pressed home his advantage. Collins was still adamant that the Unionists must accept the decision of the Irish people, for a unitary state in the Commonwealth. Lloyd-George turned nasty. He pretended that he had always understood that Griffith spoke for the delegation as a whole, and in this matter, of peace or war each of the plenipotentiary delegates would have to sign a treaty document and undertake to recommend it, otherwise there would be no agreement.

Despite the fact that Sir James Craig had not replied to the official demand from the British Government, Lloyd-George produced two letters, one of which he said he would have to send that night to Belfast on a special train and destroyer. One was a covering letter of the Government's proposals for the future relations of Ireland and Great Britain, stating that the Irish delegation had agreed to recommend the draft Treaty for acceptance. The other stated that the Irish delegation had failed to come to an agreement and that he had no proposals to send. This would be an ultimatum for "immediate and terrible war".

The Irish delegation desperately tried to turn the discussion to the length of time in which Northern Ireland would have to decide whether or not to join the Irish Free State in the Commonwealth or not. The Irish argued that the twelve month stipulation within the treaty was too long. Within that period, the Parliament of Ulster would continue and there would be pogroms. There would be massive movements of population and refugees, an entrenched state would be established. The meeting agreed that the period in which Ulster might decide was to be reduced to one month. This concession on Lloyd-George's part was spurious because Craig and his followers were quite determined, as Lloyd-George well knew, to refuse the treaty terms anyway, but to cast the blame on the Irish delegation for any breakdown. Barton was foolishly led away from the Ulster question, on which Collins had insisted that any breakdown in the negotiations must be centralised. Replying to Birkenhead's inspired probing, Barton started to say "Our main difficulty is in regard to coming into the Empire". On a pre-arranged signal, the British delegation sprang to their feet: "We have heard enough". The talks appeared to be over. But the British were bluffing. Collins glared at Barton, and in the cab back to Hans Place, Griffith made pungent and doubtless untrue reflections on Barton's paternity.

In the afternoon they agreed to dismiss the conference and to re-assemble at ten o'clock that night for a final decision. Writing about this fateful meeting afterwards, Churchill said, "Michael Collins rose looking as though he was going to shoot someone, preferably himself. In all my life I have never seen so much pain and suffering illustrated." It was then four o'clock. Lloyd-George was about to play his final card.

The tired and dispirited Irish delegation returned to Hans Place, worn out after almost six hours of intensive argument. There they ran into an atmosphere of considerable confusion, fraught with a little acrimony. There was a distinct coldness between Collins, and Griffith, who went to his room, a lonely figure. Collins was surrounded immediately by advisors. Erskine Childers was extremely vocal for rejection of the British terms, balanced on the other side by the sinister and saturnine figure of Tim Healy, who endeavoured to wear Collins' argument down by saying that whatever the defects of the Treaty were, it was a stepping stone to freedom.

Just then, after they had only been in the Hans Place Headquarters for a few minutes, a Rolls Royce arrived at the door and Lady Hazel Lavery swept in. In the back seat of the car was Lady Moya Llewellyn-Davis. Lady Lavery linked Collins and said "Michael, Please come quick. John wants to talk to you." Collins shook her off impatiently, but she whispered something in his ear at which he looked at her with a keen glance and followed her out of the room and got into the back of the car. They drove rapidly to the Laverys' luxurious mansion. Moya's face was pale and wan, her eyes were damp and there was a look of desperation in them. Inside the Laverys' house, Sir John first attempted to discuss the rights and wrongs and the advisability of signing a treaty, no matter what the terms were. But Collins lost his temper and rejected what he regarded as interference. Sir John went up to his studio. The drawing room of the Lavery's house then, had only Hazel and Moya and Collins, but beyond the folding doors to the conservatory, was the tinkling of a piano. Hazel opened one of the doors. A tall young boy of about nine years of age was playing the piano and looking out at the drizzling rain in the back garden. He had a bushy shock of brown hair and keen grey eyes. It was young Richard Llewellyn-Davies. It was a poignant moment, and Collins and Moya looked at their child with strained and tragic faces, as Hazel told them of the threat that had emanated from Lloyd-George's quarters.

That first part of the British plan was, that if there was to be immediate and terrible war to be waged upon the Irish, the Irish Government would be first destroyed and divided. An enormous propaganda attack was to made immediately upon Collins and papers were already in preparation to be sent to the gutter press in England. A plan had been made in the House of Commons to circulate the story. It was to be made known that Collins had a son and that Moya was the mother. It would then be necessary to force Crompton Llewellyn-Davis to divorce her and she would be an outcast in the London society where she had formerly been a princess. But above all, immediate arrangements had been made to unleash Tim Healy and his cohorts in Ireland against Collins, and, Hazel Lavery said, "to do what he did on Parnell before".

The reference to Parnell struck Collins like a thunderbolt. He knew immediately the importance and the danger of the British plan. With the whole

British establishment against him on one side of the Irish Sea and all the news-papers, and on the other side, Tim Healy and the bishops and all the forces of sanctimony that would be laid against him, together with those who would object to the political steps that he was now taking, on the Republican side – the "Sea Green Incorruptibles", he realised in a second that he was lost and worse, Ireland was lost. Lloyd-George was going to detonate the unity of the Republic, the Volunteers, the IRB, and Sinn Féin, with this one bombshell! All would be confusion, anger, division, recrimination. History would record for a hundred years that Michael Collins had thrown away Ireland's chance of freedom for a woman's body! He was unable to think clearly.

The young boy ceased playing his scales, and withdrew, smiling at his mother and her friends. Collins went over to the marble fireplace and put his head against it. Hazel and Moya watched him in fascination. Collins groaned, "Oh! God, if a break was to come, it was to come on Ulster. It was to come over partition. We were all determined on that." The two women, both of whom had loved him, and one of them, Moya, had loved him greatly, gazed at him in anguish. He clenched his hands until the nails welted into his palms. "They have me! They have me!" Beads of sweat were on his forehead. For a long moment he gazed out the window into the gloom of the London evening. "That long whore will stand aside with a sour smile on his gob, while the dogs are unleashed to destroy me. They think they have me!"

"What can you do?" said Hazel, "If you let them away with this they will destroy you."

Collins squared his shoulders and tossed his head, with an angry flash in his eyes, "I won't let them away with it. I won't let them destroy me. I will sign this scrap of paper and I will build an Irish army and I will take what steps I can towards Irish freedom, and if they think that they have silenced me or trapped me or spancelled me on the question of Ulster, they have never made a bigger mistake in their lives. I will show that Welsh dog what duplicity is. I will fix his Boundary Commission – all Ulster west of the Bann and south of the Mournes will be part of the Free State. I'll leave them little. I'll send every spare rebel and loose gun up North for the next three years and they'll have chaos and ashes for this."

Greatly moved, the two women went to him and both embraced him and for a long moment the three laced their arms about each other. There were tears in all their eyes.

In the midst of her tears, and her genuine emotion for Collins, Hazel Lavery felt a small gleam of triumph. If Collins signed the treaty, all would be well. As promised, Lloyd-George and Churchill and her glittering friends on both sides of the Irish Sea would be her guests when she was the lady of the viceregal lodge – the first lady of Ireland – a long way for the little Martyn girl from Chicago! Collins could be talked around later.

Back at Hans Place, Collins announced very briefly that he had decided to sign the Treaty and summoned the delegation to come with him back to

Downing Street. They were a hour late and the British Cabinet delegation had been wondering if they were going to turn up.

After a few polite words, Griffith said that the Irish delegation had returned and decided to agree the terms of the treaty as drafted, but there were some minor technical matters that they wished to discuss. The British delegation looked at each other. Lloyd-George and Churchill masked their feelings of triumph, realising the emotional tension of the moment, scattered papers around the great table and sat down to discuss minor matters for a few moments, following which each of the delegations signed draft copies of the Treaty between Ireland and England, with the intention of ending the 750 year war.

SEVENTEEN

The Split

When they signed the treaty at half past two, on the morning of 6 December, Galloper Smith, Lord Birkenhead, with whom Collins had reached a somewhat extraordinary degree of cordiality said, "I may have signed my political death warrant tonight." Collins sighed and said, "Is that so?, I think I have signed my actual death warrant." The remark was prophetic. Now began Collins's nightmare. Back in Ireland, the worst sides of the Irish character began to show as a storm of division and acrimony swept the country, and the old sow started to eat her farrow.

When the news of the treaty reached Dublin and was prematurely printed in the *Evening Mail*, great annoyance was caused in the Cabinet, and the next morning before the three absent Cabinet members arrived back in Dublin, there was a Cabinet meeting, at which a call was made for the resignation of Collins, Barton and Griffith. Cosgrave said that they should wait to see what the delegates had to say first. However, a statement was issued by the President as follows:

> "In view of the nature of the proposed Treaty with Great Britain, President De Valera has sent a urgent summons to the members of the Cabinet in London to report at once, so that a Cabinet decision may be taken. The hour of the meeting is fixed for noon tomorrow, Thursday. A meeting of the Dáil will be summoned later."

The delegates arrived in Dun Laoghaire, and were greeted by an Army reception of senior members of the IRB, who were members of the Dáil and GHQ staff. Collins took Tom Cullen aside to ask, "What are our fellows saying?" Cullen replied with the words that were to re-echo many people's thoughts, "What's good enough for you, is good enough for them." However, it was far from good enough for the rest of the Cabinet. De Valera was extremely annoyed that the delegates had not referred back to him before signing the treaty as Griffith had promised to do, and in all the weeks afterwards, no one ever thought of asking how often during all the delicate and tortuous discussions with the British, some delegates had come home at weekends, and others had made use of the telephone, even though communications were open to the British Government who were always listening in. The inconclusive Cabinet meeting, the weekend before the treaty was signed, was rarely referred to, and only to emphasise the feeling against the oath to the King.

The intense argument on the treaty raged all day in the Cabinet, and there was also some prominent members of the Government who were not immediately involved. Kevin O'Higgins put forward the viewpoint that he "did not like the Treaty, which he felt should not have been signed, but since it had been signed, we were committed to it and it should be supported" He stressed the necessity for national unity. Collins said that the position was that the contest was between the big Empire and a small nation, and the settlement was as far as any small nation could go, but that we would get more. It was a stepping stone. It was the "freedom to achieve freedom". In the end, Cosgrave had the casting vote in the Cabinet, voting with Colllins, Griffith and Barton against De Valera, Brugha and Stack.

A strong appeal was made to the President not to oppose the decision publicly because of the consequences and leave the matter to the Dáil. However, De Valera let it be known publicly that he was opposed to the Treaty, and would fight it in the Cabinet and the Dáil.

Collins had approached the first meeting in Cabinet on returning to Dublin after signing the Treaty with considerable trepidation. He expected animosity and rejection from Cathal Brugha and Austin Stack, but he did not know to what extent De Valera would also commit himself to the rejection of the treaty, knowing the consequences thereof, and he was taken by surprise by the degree of acrimony at the Cabinet meeting. When the Cabinet supported the Treaty by four to three, technically, it was a victory for Collins and the treaty. He realised that this was just the first shot, the opening battle of what would, probably, be civil war. After the meeting, he went exhausted, dispirited, physically and emotionally worn out, to his one secure haven, Furry Park in Killester, where Moya had returned the previous day.

Four days after the treaty was signed, the Supreme Council of the Brotherhood meet to consider the position. There were mixed feelings. Most members of the council agreed that the more obnoxious provisions of the draft Treaty had been changed to Ireland's advantage, and noted with approval that the oath had assumed the change suggested by the IRB. There was disappointment that the treaty ports be retained for British naval use, and the continuance of the Unionist government in the North, then in the throes of a murderous pogrom against the Catholics in the Belfast Shipyard and certain key parliamentary constituencies, was a bitter pill to swallow. It was swallowed, on Collins' assurance that the probable life of the six counties government was about three years, during which the National Army would be built up to an impressive strength of 20,000, made up mainly from the Flying Columns and be supported by one hundred thousand part-time volunteers in the IRA, North and South.

Strong and principled opposition to the whole Treaty package came from Liam Lynch, the second most influential Brother. Lynch was not playing politics – he never did and had a thinly disguised contempt for practitioners of the ancient craft. He was certainly not allying himself with De Valera whom he regarded as a contemptible and unprincipled bungler, pursuing factional interests and selling out the Republic. Lynch's case was that the Treaty was premature. The IRA was winning the war, and it should have continued for another year and final victory would be attained. The negotiations should cease and the Treaty be repudiated.

The opposition from Liam Lynch, the South Munster Divisional member of the Council, was quite important, because not only was he an IRB representative, but he was also the O/C of the First Southern Division of the IRA, which comprised of almost one quarter of the total Army's fighting strength, over 30,000 volunteers. Before the meeting of the Council, he had given an ominous indication of the possibility of civil war when, that morning, he handed to the Chief of Staff, General Richard Mulcahy, a statement from all the commanding officers of the First Southern Division, all of whom were also members of the IRB, saying that they would not accept the Treaty, and Lynch personally refused to obey the policy instructions of the IRB and transmit statements through it to the Division.

The majority of the members of the Supreme Council then and later, felt that the present Treaty terms were the best attainable and should be accepted. So strong was Lynch's opposition, expressed with eloquence and passion, that the Council decided that the IRB should not take any action officially for or against the Treaty. Even Collins was unable to persuade the Council to make a decision and it is apparent that the general feeling was that the IRB organisation must be preserved against a split at all costs. However, it was an abdication of leadership on the most important question they were ever to discuss. A month later, the IRB split, after the Dáil accepted the Treaty by a narrow margin.

In the course of the discussion in the Supreme Council, there were strong efforts made to maintain the unity of the Brotherhood and it was finally decided that the IRB would not take official action for or against the Treaty. However, members of the IRB who were also members of Dáil Éireann were circulated two days later with a letter from the Secretary, Sean O'Muirthuile, stating that the Council had decided that the Treaty should be ratified, but the Dáil members were given freedom of action in the matter. This note was untrue and misleading and infuriated Lynch.

A further letter was sent a few days later, saying the Council had decided not to oppose the Treaty or support it, and this was circulated to all the Centres of the IRB, and at the same time, attention was drawn to the traditional policy of the Brotherhood, which was to make use of all instruments, political or military, which related to attaining freedom and an independent Ireland. But this note did not stifle the growing discontent and opposition to the Treaty, which was beginning to swell in the ranks of the IRB, the GHQ staff and the members of the Dáil.

The next day was the first meeting of the Dáil. Unfortunately, it was not an occasion where people sought to discover truth or demonstrate their strength.

The whole background of that unhappy time was a source of national shame, but must be read dispassionately, in an attempt to understand the whirlwind that was about to overcome the Irish people. The debate boiled over into acrimonious discussions regarding the ephemeral symbols of nothingness, the oaths to the crown, whilst almost ignoring the practical reality of the partition of Ulster, and the creation of a brutal military dictatorship there, already beginning to divide and rule by pogrom and discrimination.

On December 8, De Valera had issued a proclamation declaring that he would not recommend acceptance of the agreement:

> "A Charda Gaedhal **[Irish spelling]**,
>
> You have seen in the public press the text of the proposed Treaty with Great Britain.
>
> The terms of the agreement are in violent conflict with the wishes of the majority of this nation as expressed freely in successive elections during the last three years.
>
> I feel it my duty to inform you immediately that I cannot recommend the acceptance of this Treaty, neither to Dáil Éireann or to the country. In this attitude, I am supported by the Ministers of Home Affairs and Defence.
>
> The public session of Dáil Éireann has been set up for Wednesday next at 11 o'clock. I ask the people to maintain, during the interval, the same discipline as here to fore. Members of the Cabinet, of divided opinions, are prepared to carry on the public services as usual.
>
> The Army, as such, of course, is not effected by the political situation and continues under the same orders and control.
>
> The greatest test of our people has come. Let us face it worthily, without bitterness and, above all, without recrimination. There is a definite Constitutional way of resolving our political differences. Let us not depart from it and let the conduct of the Cabinet in this matter be an example to the whole nation."

The release of this statement, of course, caused an enormous amount of bitterness and recrimination.

On the day of the Dáil meeting, the *Irish Independent* published statements by 15 members of the Irish hierarchy, giving the proposed treaty their full support. But the divided opinions of the Supreme Council of the IRB were beginning to be echoed throughout the membership of the Brotherhood, with disastrous consequences. The iron discipline which had carried the IRB to ultimate victory in the Anglo-Irish War was cracking under the pressures of the British tactics of partial peace. A considerable number of members were in favour of supporting Collins, President and Head Centre, in favour of the

Treaty, but there were different interpretations of how the decision would be accepted. Most significantly of all, General Liam Lynch, who was the most powerful officer in the IRA, vigorously opposed the treaty and recommendation, and insisted that he would not recognise it and would campaign against it throughout the country. It was the first fissure in the Council, and in a very short time it would lead to a widening wedge in the ranks of the Brotherhood, which was to prove disastrous.

The debate in the Dáil ended in a narrow victory for the pro-treaty group, led by Collins and Griffiths, but the split was only beginning. Within a very short time, all three sections of the national movement, the Irish Republican Brotherhood, the Army of the Irish Republic and Sinn Féin Party, were to conduct similar discussions, and in each case, a split was to take place, which was to emerge and be reflected in the votes of the deputies of the Dáil, and, of course, in the minds of the people of the country.

Following the Dáil vote to approve the treaty by 64 votes to 57, De Valera resigned and led his followers out of the house. The remaining members of the Dáil approved a new government with Griffith as President, with Michael Collins as Minister for Finance, Cosgrave as Minister for Local Government, Gavin Duffy as Minister for Foreign Affairs, Kevin O'Higgins as Minister for Economic Affairs and Richard Mulcahy as Minister for Defence.

On 14 January, another new government was formed by the members of the Dáil excluding DeValera's 57 deputies, and including for the first time four Unionist members returned by Dublin University. This was the interim or Provisional Government, provided for by the Treaty to undertake the necessary constitutional arrangements and to accept the various State assets in the 26 Counties from the British. Collins was the Chairman of the Provisional Government and this second cabinet included Duggan, O'Higgins, Cosgrave, Eoin MacNeill, Joe McGrath, Fionan Lynch, and PJ Hogan.

There was a dubious air about these proceedings and by no democratic criteria can the Free State Provisional Government be said to have been legally elected. But it had *de facto* office, and the political, military and financial support of the British.

An early indication of British support was the formal handing over to Collins, as Chairman of Dublin Castle. This was an emotional occasion for many and tangible proof that times had changed. Although Churchill had bad mouthed the change by his famous phrase "We are governing Ireland with an economy of English lives" the British power that had ruled from this grim stone castle for 700 years was now handed over to the foremost Son of the Revolution.

The Last Viceroy, Fitzalan is supposed to have gently chided Collins on the occasion "You are seven minutes late Mr Collins". Collins retorted "We've been waiting 700 years, you can have another seven minutes". And when welcomed by the Under Secretary and General Boyd with the words "We're glad to see you Mr Collins". Collins replied in his most affected broad Cork drawl "Like hell ye are, Boys". These stories, whether true or not, were told all over Ireland within a month.

The Provisional Government of the Irish Free State, and the new Government of the Second Dáil of the Irish Republic, with which it was a co-terminous parasite, then proceeded to take possession of as much British Government property as possible, and to proceed with the other requirements of the Treaty. But it was not plain sailing.

The split had its most dangerous manifestations in the IRA from February onwards. The British military posts were gradually evacuated throughout the country and handed over to the detachments of the local IRA, usually with military courtesy and an "Eyes Right", as the two units would pass each other, but sometimes there was ill-will and acrimony, as the departing British troops damaged installations, usually lavatories. There was a continual political shuffle within the ranks of the IRA, now some 124,000 strong, as local commanders swung in their sympathies, pro and anti-Treaty. This was reflected in an unseemly rush to occupy key positions and barracks, sometimes to the confusion of the retreating British, who were often unsure to whom they should hand over the barracks they had defended in the late War against the new tenants.

The Sinn Féin Party held an Ard Fheis on 21 February, and agreed that no vote on the treaty would be taken by the delegates, and that the required General Election not be held until June. It was clear the feelers were out for a compromise between Collins and De Valera.

It was proposed by the IRA Executive, and sanctioned by the Dáil Cabinet on 27 February, that a General Army Convention be held, under the aegis of GHQ, to consider the question of the treaty and the army unity. Many meetings were held between opposing groups of officers to search for a formula to maintain the fragile unity of the IRA, and for a while it seemed that opposition to the treaty would eventually consolidate into parliamentary and constitutional methods. Collins had strong hope that a formula would be found to merge the Flying Columns and Divisional and GHQ staffs of the IRA with the embryo Free State National Army.

But there were influences at work, dedicated to increasing tension and bitterness to extremes, and unfortunately the Dáil Cabinet announced on 15 March that the proposed convention was proscribed, and that all officers and men were forbidden to attend. This was a disastrous mistake.

Immediately, the more moderate commandants lost all influence in the wavering IRA to Rory O'Connor, Liam Lynch and Ernie O'Malley. The Convention was held, thus repudiating the authority of the Dáil, and elected a new Executive, which was a thinly-disguised IRA military government in embryo. Soon after, the Executive occupied the Four Courts for their headquarters, and the path to Civil War was clearly outlined to all.

At his stage De Valera, chafing at his impotence and insignificance on the political stage, announced that he was forming a new political Party called Cumann na Poblachta, composed of the Anti-Treaty members of the second

Dáil. No one took the slightest notice. Desperate, he then made an extreme radical swing, and attempted to curry favour with the IRA executive, who despised him, by bloodthirsty public endorsements of their position.

In Dungarvan, on 16 March, he announced ...

> "The Treaty . . . barred the way to independence with the blood of fellow Irishmen. It is only by Civil War after this that they could get their independence. If you don't fight today, you will have to fight to-morrow and I say, when you are in a good fighting position, then fight on."

The next day, St Patrick's Day, reviewing a parade of seven hundred IRA men of Carrick-on-Suir, he said:

> "If the Treaty was accepted, the fight for freedom would still go on: and the Irish people instead of fighting foreign soldiers would have to fight the Irish soldiers of an Irish government, set up by Irishmen. If the Treaty was not rejected, perhaps it was over the bodies of the young men he saw around him that day that the fight for Irish freedom may be fought."

Again, at Thurles he reached the nadir of treachery to the concept of demo-cratic government in saying:

> "If they accepted the Treaty, and if the Volunteers of the future tried to complete the work the Volunteers of the past four years had been at-tempting, they would have to complete it, not over the bodies of foreign soldiers but over the dead bodies of their own countrymen. They would have to wade through, perhaps, the blood of some of the members of the Government in order to get Irish freedom."

At Killarney, 9 March, he again said:

> "If we continue on this movement which was begun when the Volun-teers were started, and we suppose this Treaty is ratified by your votes, then these men, in order to achieve freedom will have, as I said yester-day, to march over the dead bodies of their own brothers. They will have to wade through Irish blood. . . ."

But this windy posturing for Republican support was greeted with the silent contempt it deserved by the IRA executive. The entire Republican leadership was to be liquidated and the country to endure a fratricidal civil war before De Valera achieved any political recognition, and that over the bones of the Republican movement which he was, in turn, to persecute to the most malignant of his ability. Appalled at the prospect of Civil War, ten senior officers, including Collins, Mulcahy and Tom Hales, met and drafted a call for Army unity and agreed elections with the intention of forming a national government.

This "Army Document" was read to the Dáil, but Griffith was cool towards it and the Four Courts executive rejected it roundly. The document was, a short time later, to be the basis of the Collins/De Valera pact, the last hope of averting Civil War. On the day, 22 May, that the document was read to the Dáil by Sean O'Hagarty, by special permission since he was not a member, the Dáil appointed a committee to try to promote a settlement. Five were from the pro-Treaty side, Sean Hales, Seamus O'Dwyer, Sean MacEoin, Joseph McGuinness and Patrick O'Maille. Five were from the anti-Treaty side; Harry Boland, Liam Mellowes, Tom Clarke, Sean Moylan and PJ Ruttledge.

Although the Griffith/O'Higgins sector of the "National Free State Provisional Government", and the IRA garrison in the Four Courts protested against it, the majority of the members of the Dáil were anxious to explore any possibility rather than war. Collins and De Valera were urged to consult together, and for three tense days they battled out in colourful polemic. On 20 May 1922, the Collins/De Valera Pact saw the light of day: It infuriated the British, the IRA, and the more extreme Free Staters, but for a short time it offered the hope that brothers in arms might yet be prevented from slaying each other.

There was to be a National Coalition Panel for the Dáil election. All candidates would be designated as Sinn Féin, and the existing strength of the Pro and Anti Treaty sentiment in the Dáil would be returned unopposed. The Government to be elected would have an elected President, a Minister of Defence representing the IRA GHQ, and nine other ministers, five from the majority faction, and four from the minority. It was stated the "the National Position requires the entrusting of the Government of the Country into the joint hands of those who have been the strength of the national situation during the last few years, without prejudice to their present respective positions." Also, "every and other interest is free to go up and contest the election equally with the Sinn Féin Panel."

The election was held on 16 June, and the new Dáil was due to assemble on 30 June. The result was a victory for Collins, Griffith and the Treaty Party, the people voting decisively for peace at any price. 58 Pro-Treaty deputies were returned, 35 Anti-Treaty. Four Unionists were elected unopposed for Trinity College. Farmers Party and Independents won seven seats each, and Labour returned 17 deputies.

In accordance with the pact, the Government would have contained four ministers from the Anti-Treaty side, and probably seven from the supporters of the Treaty, including Collins as president. It was just possible that this ad-hoc Coalition could have threaded its way through the minefield to Peace, and eventually normal political controversy and democratic decision, but the Dáil and Government envisaged in the Collins\De Valera pact was never to meet.

Andy Cope, the indefatigable conspirator and spook-in-chief, was in constant communication with Lloyd-George, who realised that his own tenure of Downing Street was imperilled by events in Dublin. Threads were pulled together, military chiefs were alerted, and important meetings were held to influence the more malleable of the Free State Cabinet.

Britain could not afford to tolerate peace with Rory O'Connor and the Four Courts IRA, and the inception of a Coalition Government of Pro and Anti Treatyites would be regarded as a breach of the Treaty.

There were ominous mutterings about re-occupying Dublin, and naval bombardment.

In 1993, the release of State Papers in London indicated the scope and menace of the preparations made by General Boyd at this time, and these were made known to O'Higgins, McNeill and the wavering section in the Provisional Government, who realised that their own brief tenure of office was drawing to an inexorable close. Detailed plans had been drawn up to occupy certain towns, to expel the inhabitants, and to relocate the loyalist population there in protected centres. These loyalists would be armed and carry out the expulsions of the existing inhabitants, an early example of what is now known as "ethnic cleansing". The rest of the country would then become a Free-Fire-Zone under martial law.

At the moment when cool heads and a period of relaxation were most needed, a bolt from the blue turned all calculations upside down, and gave Ireland's bitterest enemies the provocation they needed.

EIGHTEEN

Civil War

In the last week of June, 1922, affairs suddenly accelerated and political tension rose. On the morning of Thursday, 22 June, two men arrived at the front door of Sir Henry Wilson's house in London. The Field Marshal was just then entering the door himself and was shot dead. The two assassins ran off, but they were hampered by the fact that one of them had an artificial leg, and were quickly surrounded by an angry mob of Londoners. The two men, Dunne and O'Sullivan, were arrested. Dunne was the Head Centre of the IRB in London. The British establishment writhed in fury. Sir Henry was a Member of Parliament, he was a chief advisor of the Unionists, a Field Marshal, and a former Chief of the Imperial General Staff. He was also the author of the "Burn them out" plan of the Unionist government for dealing with the unduly large nationalist minority in some strategic electoral constituencies, which was and is still a major plank in Unionist strategy, as witnessed in 1935 and 1969. But the repercussions of this killing were to broaden out and poison relationships between Ireland and England.

The killing of Wilson had been ordered by Michael Collins, two months before, as a reprisal for the continuing murder of Catholics in Belfast, where whole families such as the McMahons had been wiped out in the pogrom, and leading Unionist politicians and business men, such as Twaddell, were shot, according to this fatal order, which had not been cancelled in the confusion and stress of the ferment in Dublin, arising from the split. The immediate direct effect of the shootings on the situation in Belfast was to cause the pogrom to be turned off like a tap. Once the Orange leaders realised that the retaliation would not be at street level, but on the highest in the community, and since none was higher than the Field Marshal, they all feared for their lives. The campaign of murder was discontinued, but, in retrospect, the shooting of Wilson was an untimely and very foolish decision, which quite literally unleashed the dogs of war once again in Ireland.

The next day, 23 June, Lloyd-George wrote a clear ultimation to Collins, that unless he took immediate and proper action against the IRA Four Courts Garrison, the treaty would be held to be violated and the British Government would be free to take whatever military action they thought proper. The British offered military assistance to the Provisional Government. At this stage, the Provisional Government was still a committee elected by its own supporters only. The elected Free State Dáil to which it was to be responsible and which would endorse its formation, had not yet met. In fact, the last meeting of the Dáil was to have taken place on the 30 June and the Free State Dáil was to meet on 1 July to ratify the existence of the Government. However, the committee which had taken power, in the name of the Provisional movement, did not allow the Parliament to meet until 9 September, by which time, many of the principals on both sides were dead, and there was little opposition in that Parliament. The Sinn Féin deputies who had voted against the Treaty still abstained from attendance.

Collins did not receive the letter from Lloyd-George, being himself absent on tour of Munster, inspecting Army Garrisons. The Provisional Government, mainly Griffith and O'Higgins, replied that the information to which Lloyd-George had referred in his letter as being in the possession of the British Government, regarding the assassination of Wilson, should be placed at their disposal. The British immediately telegraphed back that this information was highly secret and could not be disclosed. The same day, they summoned General McCready to Downing Street. He was asked if the Four Courts could be occupied at once by the British troops. He said it could, but he strongly opposed such a decision. Griffith had issued a statement denouncing "this anarchic deed" and he met in conference with senior British officers to discuss the position. According to the *Guardian* report of that day, "A conference was held in Dublin yesterday, at which Mr Arthur Griffith, Mr Andy Cope, the Assistant Under Secretary, Major General Dalton of the Provisional Army, and two senior British generals, were present, to consider the continued occupation of the Four Courts by the insurgents, under General Rory O'Connor. The proceedings were secret."

The next day McCready came back to Dublin, and when he was going over details of the scheme for the British occupation of the Four Courts with General Boyd, whose troops would carry out the operation, another telegram came ordering it to be put into effect the next day, 25 June. Preparation were accordingly made for the return of British troops to Dublin streets in full military paraphernalia.

However, the following morning, word came through from London, that the Government had reconsidered their original decision and that no action was to be taken against the Four Courts. McCready said, "I have never ceased to congratulate myself of having been instrumental in the staving off on what would have been a disaster." The Army Council and the Cabinet, with the exception of the originator of the scheme, Winston Churchill, heaved a sigh of relief that wiser counsel prevailed.

The wiser counsel was to accept the decision of the secret meeting between Griffith, Dalton, Cope and the two British generals, and the decision was that the Provisional Army, the Free State Army, would better do the job. They would be armed with British artillery and given maximum support.

The decision was not agreed to by Michael Collins, but despite his strenuous efforts to calm the situation, there was nothing he could do about it. He did however, instruct Dalton that before he opened fire on the Four Courts, he was to cut off gas, electricity and water supplies, prevent any food from reaching the garrison and wait until they surrendered. Dalton did not carry out these orders. Cope, in addition to being Assistant Under Secretary, and Lloyd-George's political instrument, was also de facto chief of all intelligence operations, and was, by far, the most powerful British Officer in Ireland. He controlled all agents directly, including Dalton, and insisted on an early attack. He was determined that the Free State Army and the IRA should be brought into armed conflict.

The next day, the Four Courts executive decided that a convoy under Peadar O'Donnell would be sent to the North. A further significant move was that friendly approaches were made to Liam Lynch and the other members of the executive who were still staying at the Clarence Hotel, and the divisions between them and the Four Courts staff were overcome and friendly relations were established. Liam Lynch again assumed his position as Chief of Staff of the IRA. The Republicans lumbered unthinkingly towards a civil war, which they could not hope to win.

Things got worse on Monday, 26 June. The House of Commons met, "hungry with anti-Irish fury". Bonar Law, the leader of the Conservatives, expressed his views with intense passion to the Prime Minister, Lloyd-George, and to Winston Churchill, and they realised that they must answer to the Empire for the death of Sir Henry Wilson, or yield office forthwith to a Conservative Government. Churchill eloquently attempted to direct the storm of blame towards the IRA, who had nothing to do with Wilson's death, and who had issued a statement to that effect. He threatened immediate military action and stated that the Free State Provisional Government had now been adequately equipped with war materials and artillery. Lloyd-George endorsed this view and stated, "I do not want to give the House any details of the communications which we have sent to the Provisional Government. I would rather they acted on their own initiative, rather than with the appearance that they are doing it under compulsion from a British Government."

Unfortunately, the same day, a Four Courts section of the IRA was sent out to commandeer 16 cars recently imported from Belfast by Ferguson Motors. The order was given partly to enforce the Belfast boycott, imposed as a counter to the pogrom against nationalists and catholics there, and partly to promote transport for Peadar O'Donnell's Flying Column which was being organised to go North. The order was carried out and the cars were seized. The IRA O/C, Leo Henderson, was arrested on this operation by Provisional army troops. A committee of IRA officers called immediately to Beggars Bush Barracks to protest at Henderson's arrest and demand his release. They were assured that Henderson would receive treatment proper to a prisoner-of-war officer and would be released on parole. However, it was discovered that night that Henderson had been lodged in Mountjoy Prison as a car thief. The Four Courts Garrison decided to take a high military hostage in reprisal and a party was sent to arrest the Deputy Chief of Staff of the Provisional Army, General Ginger O'Connell, who was in charge of training. He was captured and brought to the Four Courts and detained as a prisoner-of-war officer, with all honour, eating with his captors and being properly treated. Beggars Bush Headquarters was informed that he would be detained as a hostage until Leo Henderson was released. This was really twisting the lion's tail, and was used as a provocation by the Provisional Government for the attack on the Four Courts.

The next day, Tuesday, 27 June, there was further activity in the Four Courts in preparation for the Northern column of 16 cars. They were armed and provisioned, and the intention was to leave at dawn the next morning. The Provisional Government issued a statement denouncing the stealing of the 16 cars, the capture of Lieutenant General Ginger O'Connell, and other reckless and criminal acts which had disturbed the country, and concluded, "The Government is determined that the country shall no longer be held up from the pursuits of its normal life and the re-establishment of its free national institutions. It calls, therefore, for all citizens to co-operative actively with them in the measures that they are taking to ensure the public safety and to secure Ireland for the Irish People."

At 2 a.m. the following morning, the streets around the Four Courts were filled with Provisional troops. They drove armoured cars against the gates, blocking the exits. Rory O'Connor insisted that the garrison should not open fire first. Two 18 pounder guns, lent to Dalton by General McCready, were placed in position across the Liffey from the Four Courts. At 3.40 a.m., the Commander of the garrison received a note from Brigadier General Tom Ennis on behalf of the Provisional Government troops, demanding surrender of the Four Courts by four o'clock. The garrison agreed to march out by 8 a.m., but the Dogs of War were not to be denied their bone. At seven minutes past four, the guns opened fire on the Four Courts and the Civil War had begun. Collins disappeared from public view for a few days, mourning the end of his hopes for a peaceful solution to the split. The IRB had not learned that the most abstruse intellectual discussions and conspiracies can be set at naught by one quick slash of a sword.

All that day and the next five days, there was fierce fighting in Dublin. Oscar Traynor arrived with the Dublin Brigade and occupied the east side of O'Connell Street, the wrong side, in an attempt to penetrate the cordon of the Four Courts without success. Liam Lynch succeeded in escaping to Heuston Station to get a train south. He was stopped and questioned by officers of the Provisional Army who communicated with Mulcahy. Lynch gave evasive answers and satisfied Mulcahy that he would be neutral in the conflict, and he was permitted to take the train south. However, when he reached Clonmel, he established the headquarters of the IRA and formally began the military campaign of the Civil War in Munster, as Chief of Staff of the IRA.

By the evening of 30 June, the east side of O'Connell Street was in ruins from the artillery fire of the new Artillery Division of the Free State Army, which had been lent to them by the British. There was a very large explosion in the Four Courts, which blew off the dome and destroyed an enormous amount of priceless historical records and deeds. The garrison surrendered.

On the way to prison, Ernie O'Malley escaped to take control of the 2nd Eastern Division of the IRA. The Government agreed formally to treat the prisoners as prisoners-of-war and military captives, under the rules of the Geneva Convention. The prisoners included, Rory O'Connor, Liam Mellowes, Dick Barrett, and Joe McKelvey, all members of the Supreme Council of the IRB. The Hamman Hotel was severely damaged and the garrison escaped, some to surrender and some to escape through the top of O'Connell Street. The last man in the burning ruins was Cathal Brugha. He refused to surrender, as he had also refused in 1916, and came rushing out of the hotel shooting against the cordon of Provisional soldiers, who fired at him with rifles and machine guns and he fell dead opposite the GPO.

This was the day that the Dáil was to have met for the last time to finalise details of its transfer of power to the Provisional Government, the Parliament of which was to meet the next day, 1 July.

However, it suited neither the British nor the ruling cabal in the Free State Provisional cabinet to allow either Dáil or Provisional Parliament to meet until interfering peacemakers were neutralised, and the Civil War in full spate. In the Republican political theology, which has persisted to this day, the independent second Dáil never went out of existence. The second Dáil did not formally ever hand over its power, never having met to do so. The few remaining living members of it finally surrendered their legislative power to the IRA Army Council in 1939, which of course, they had no shadow of right to do. But these irrelevant theological abstract arguments had nothing what ever to do with the war on the ground, which went very, very badly indeed for the Republicans.

The Brotherhood, by now, was splintered and ineffective, as the divided armies attempted vainly to settle political polemics by the gun. Only the public admiration of Collins as leader and victor in the Anglo-Irish War remained its main asset.

Collins, by this time, was back in Dublin, to meet a great deal of suspicion and hostility from the other members of the Provisional Government, of which he was Chairman. Griffith and others suspected that he had had a hand in the execution of Wilson, and O'Higgins used this to undermine Collins's position, playing on Griffith's suspicions. At this stage, the once strong Republican movement had been split into a number of factions. On the extreme side, were those with Liam Lynch, who were now waging a war against the Provisional Government. Their nominal political leader was De Valera, but he had no authority and absolutely no influence on events for some considerable time, being treated with undisguised contempt by Liam Lynch and the IRB members who had broken with Collins.

But in the Provisional Government itself, there were also factions. As far as the public and the media were concerned, the leading and popular men were Collins and Griffiths, who were trusted by the population, and Collins was the people's hero. The other members of the Provisional Government were faceless men, unknown, except for Richard Mulcahy. But the truth, at the time, was the fact that the Provisional Government had only the most tenuous legal authority, but it had de facto power, and British financial and military support, and within this fluid position, two very different groups were manoeuvring for position.

One of those was the IRB group of Collins, Mulcahy and McGrath, whose policy was based on using the treaty as a stepping stone for eventual freedom. They realised that the undisciplined IRA was an immediate threat which had to be met and the maximum effort would have to be made to establish the authority of the Provisional Government, by prosecuting the Civil War with the utmost speed and strength, before proceeding to the next stepping stone.

But the other members of the Provisional Government, were a group comprising O'Higgins, Cosgrave, McNeill and Blythe. They were intent on bringing the Republic, and as many Republicans as possible with it, down into destruction, and settling down to play their part within the Empire. The chief political adviser was the saturnine figure of Tim Healy, "the bitterest tongue in Ireland", who was soon to get his reward of the Vice Regal Lodge in the Phoenix Park, crowning a life of treachery and deceit. But all this time the people did not know that Griffith was not a member of the Provisional Government, but was in fact, President of the outgoing Dáil, which was no longer, legally, in existence. For the moment, Collins was politically vulnerable, from the shooting of Wilson, and the O'Higgins faction rapidly moved to weaken and dislodge the IRB faction within the Government.

On 12 July, there was an extraordinary meeting of the Provisional Government, at which Collins was removed from the position of Chairman and replaced by William Cosgrave. Collins was, in fact, also removed from the Government and was no longer a member of the Provisional Cabinet. The Cabinet then consisted of O'Higgins, Cosgrave and the other Free State figures, who were pro-British to a man, with Mulcahy and McGrath, confused and isolated. However, the Government needed Collins in public. There was no announcement made and the people never knew that Collins was no longer leader of the government and, in fact, this matter did not become widely known for almost 50 years. An innocuous statement, signed by Cosgrave as "Acting Chairman" appeared a few weeks later, but no one noticed it. The Cabinet minutes recording the ousting of Collins were later forged to infer that he had resigned, but were never signed. As late as 1970, Emmet Dalton strenuously denied that Collins had ever been ousted as Chairman of the Provisional Government, and stated that he was inspecting the army in Cork as Chairman. Later in the same interview in 1970 (with Conor McCarthaigh) Dalton tripped himself up by defending the arrangement made in the 12 July meeting by which Collins was removed as Chairman of the Provisional Government, and Mulcahy made Minister for Defence and Chief of Staff, with Collins being entitled Commander-in-Chief of the Free State Army.

A War Council had been created, partly to ease the axing of Collins, on which Collins was Commander in Chief of the Army. The other members of the Council were General Mulcahy, Chief-of-Staff, and General Eoin O'Duffy, who was Commander of the South Western Division of the Provisional Free State Army, all three being IRB Council members. Collins hoped and clearly intended that this would, in effect, be a covert IRB military Government in which he was the senior person, but the significant thing about this was that Collins was also ousted as Minister of Defence on the spurious grounds that one could not be Commander of the Army and Minister of Defence and Chairman of the Government. However, he was replaced by Mulcahy, who was Chief of Staff and Minister of Defence, and there was obviously a deliberate amount of confusion here. Mulcahy's role was ambivalent, from here on. He seemed to be, vainly seeking to protect his personal position, and his strong attachment to Collins seems to have wavered.

Collins, at this stage, regarded the Provisional Government, and the Provisional Parliament, which had never met, with a certain amount of disinterest. His activities and thoughts and actions were bound up with the new army which he had created, the Provisional Army, of which he was Commander in Chief, and he was quite well aware of the fact that his position politically was immensely stronger than Griffith, or Cosgrave. He behaved, in effect, for the next month, as if he was Military Governor of the Country, and the IRB Executive the real government, and a whispering campaign began that he intended to make himself dictator. There was little doubt he could have so done, but he did not bother at the time. The main point was the success of the war. He had laboured hard to avoid it. Now he would labour twice as hard to win it quickly, and get the nation back on the rails again. He was under great strain, and without trusted advisers, and it is easy to understand his self-deception in this final month. He was quite convinced that time was on his side, and when the Provisional Parliament met, hopefully with DeValera's contingent present, after the Civil War, there was no doubt whatever in his mind that the Parliament would have no alternative to electing him as President.

Whatever his future political plans were, his immediate path was quite clear. He was determined, to crush the IRA militarily in the field, and if the War could be over within a month, which he hoped, then he would succeed in turning the defeated IRA by giving them generous peace terms, turning them against the British in the North and getting rid of this tremendous political problem that they would pose. In the end, when the Provisional Parliament finally met, in which his supporters who were members of the IRB, would have been, quite certainly, in the majority he would have no difficulty what so ever dealing with Cosgrave and O'Higgins and the other people, who at the moment, were seeking to spancel the Provisional Free State within the confines of the Empire. His confidence was misplaced.

He had underestimated the malevolence of the British, who felt betrayed by him, and the thirst for power of O'Higgins, to whom Collins was a barrier to be removed. He had ignored the pressure of British Intelligence on Cope, and their links back to Churchill and their thirst for revenge for Bloody Sunday.

For the next five or six weeks, the Civil War developed all over the country, and steady pressure was put on the Republicans. Lynch had occupied a line which stretched from Limerick across to Waterford, and south of that line, almost all of Munster, the IRA were the dominant force. Collins moved very quickly throughout the rest of the country and occupied the main centres. Within a few days, they had arranged to send troops by sea for landings at Fenit and Passage East. Emmet Dalton landed in Passage East with 500 men, and the Republicans withdrew from Cork without firing a shot. The landing at Fenit led to the main Republican positions in Kerry being evacuated, and within a few days, the IRA had taken to the hills again to perform an ineffectual guerrilla campaign.

On 1 August, a committee known as the Peoples Rights Association had enquired of Liam Lynch on what basis peace might be discussed. This was the first peace feeler. Lynch replied, on behalf of the IRA, in a conciliatory way, "When the Provisional Government ceases their attacks on us, defending action on our part can cease. But if the Independent Dáil, which is the Government of the Republic, or any other elected assembly, carries on such a Government, I see no difficulty as to the allegiance of the Army." The next day, this confused statement was forwarded to Cosgrave. His reaction was a repudiation of the independent Dáil. He issued a statement that:

> "The Dáil came to an end on 30 June. The meeting that was to have taken place on that date would have been purely formal, with the purpose of bringing business to a conclusion. The Sovereign Assembly of Ireland was now the Parliament elected in June, whose authority these irregular troops have flouted."

This was a lie. Parliament did not meet for the first time until 9 September, and in the interim, a junta of self-appointed ministers had seized power with the collusion of the British. They were the people who were preventing the Parliament from meeting, not the "irregular troops". Collins had been deposed as Chairman of this junta by Cosgrave, but this was never made public. The people and the Army still thought that Collins and Griffith were at the helm of State, and were mollified and unaware of the totally illegal actions of the pseudo-Government.

On 2 August, there was a very significant meeting, between the senior officers of the 3rd and 4th Northern Divisions of the IRA, and Collins as Commander-in-Chief of the Free State Army. Collins presided at this extraordinary meeting, in which the CIC of one army was meeting the senior staff officers of another army, with which he was fighting a bitter war. The meeting took place in Portobello Barracks, after a delivery of 83 rifles by Collins and Tobin to Seamus Woods, the 3rd Northern Divisional Commandant. At this time, Collins was Dáil deputy for South Armagh, as well as Cork, a fact which he forcefully reminded his audience.

At that meeting, as mentioned in a letter from Seamus Woods, now in the State Papers Office (S180\1A) Collins assured the officers that his policy as CIC and as a member of Government would be of non-recognition of the Unionist government, and his intention was to make government of the Six Counties impossible until the Boundary Commission decided on the Boundary, and he was confident that most of South Armagh, South Down and the Mournes, Fermanagh, Tyrone and Derry would be transferred and ceded into the Free State by the Boundary Commission, within two years, and in the meantime he would support the Northern Republican movement with all possible resources and support, in the border areas. The Unionists could not succeed in holding the entire Six County area. To this end, as much support as possible would be given by Southern Government departments. The teachers in Nationalist areas, many of whom were in the IRA, would be paid by the Department of Education in Dublin, and the IRA would be supported by the Ministries of Defence and Finance, through IRB links.

He also made a confident prediction that the Civil War in the South would be over within a few weeks, and all Republican prisoners in the South would be held on honourable military terms, and he hoped that the bulk of them would be released by Christmas, the Northerners first. He gave his personal guarantee that the captured Four Courts Garrison would be well treated, and allowed free choice of their future political and military careers. The northern officers, most of them Brothers, and despairingly hopeful of Collins, looked on him as a saviour.

Within two days, a full report of the proceedings at this meeting was on Cope's desk, and he sent copies to Lloyd George, and also warned O'Higgins and Cosgrave. There was an urgent policy meeting in Whitehall of the ministers concerned with Ireland. Churchill was sulphurous. The shooting of Sir Henry Wilson had a different effect in London than in Belfast. Whereas the Unionists flinched from confronting the IRA in a personal campaign of political assination, the British have no qualms or doubts about their own capacity to resist such a campaign. Churchill snarled in Cabinet, "Mr Collins must find that two can play at that game". Within a week, Cope received a "Most Secret" document from Lloyd George, which contained grave instructions.

He held an urgent meeting with O'Higgins and Blythe, and warned them that Britain would re-occupy Dublin and impose martial law over all Ireland, if Collins was not removed. O'Higgins and Blythe sought time for consideration and consultation with other trusted members of the government, and this was given, but Cope warned that any attempt to make peace with the IRA would be regarded by the UK government as an act of war against Britain.

NINETEEN

The Assassins Gather

On 3 August, the day after Collins met the Northern Republican Staff, there was a tragedy that caused deep pain to Collins. The day before, Provisional Government troops had raided a hotel in Malahide after getting a tip that Harry Boland was there. Boland attempted to escape and was shot. He was unarmed and could have easily been taken prisoner, but there was a suspicion that Boland was marked down as one of the people not to be arrested. He had been appointed as a member of the Peace Committee of Dáil members in May, just three months before, and this Committee was to meet and, if possible, prevent a split from spreading and continually attempt to make peace between the warring sections.

On the anti-Treaty side, the members of this were Harry Boland, Liam Mellowes, Mrs Tom Clarke, Sean Moylan and P.J. Rutledge. On the pro-Treaty side were Sean Hales, Seamus O'Dwyer, Joseph McGuinness, Padraig O'Maille and Sean MacEoin. Boland, Mellowes and Hales were all to be killed during the Civil War. Harry Boland died the next day at St Vincent's Hospital. Michael Collins was overcome with grief, and for a day or two, was inconsolable. He poured out his grief to Kitty Kiernan, whom they both had loved.

Within a week, Emmet Dalton had entered Cork City, having cautiously advanced from Passage East. There was no Republican opposition. The same day, the last town to be held by the IRA was Fermoy, which was Liam Lynch's headquarters. Lynch burned the barracks and evacuated Fermoy. On 11 August, the IRA occupied no towns whatsoever and Liam Lynch retreated back to the hills, breaking up the divisions into guerrilla columns, to begin the endless task of ambushes and destruction, the pointless wearying, stupid civil war, which was to last for another year, and poison two generations. Dalton then made a surprise trip by train to Dublin, on receipt of a command from Cope, using family illness as an excuse.

On 12 August, when Collins was on a brief visit to Limerick, Arthur Griffith died early in the morning, bending down to tie his lace. He had been an increasingly tired and isolated figure, drinking very heavily and almost ignored by the members of the Provisional Government. He was leading a life of solitary terror, expecting that he and Collins might be assassinated any day, and it may be said that his death came as a relief to him. Neither the Dáil, of which he was President, nor the Provisional Parliament was allowed to meet, and although the people thought that the Free State Government consisted mainly of Michael Collins and Arthur Griffith, neither of them were actually members of it. The news of his death rocked Collins and he immediately returned for the funeral. His relationship with Griffith was curious. He had considerable respect and affection for the man, but Collins and he did not agree on major political questions.

Griffith distrusted Collins's wild enthusiasm. He was a much more conservative and staid figure, believing that the Empire could not be defeated, and the best Ireland could do, was to have self-government within the Empire. The Kings, Lords and Commons theory which he had first proposed in 1905, was fruitless and he died knowing that it would never happen. The Archbishop of Dublin told Collins at Griffiths funeral at Glasnevin, "You might have to prepare Michael, you might well be next".

By macabre coincidence, the day of Griffith's funeral was also the day of the hanging of Dunne and O'Sullivan in London. Collins had striven mightily and in vain to save them by political appeals to Lloyd-George, and several febrile rescue plots. His thoughts were grim on that day and photographs show his inner misery. But by 17 August 1922, the civil war was militarily over, with the almost complete military defeat of the IRA, and Collins was free to think then about peace terms. He had taught the Republicans a bitter lesson in power in only a month, and they now did not control a single Irish town. For Collins, the time was ripe to extend the hand of peace. He made contacts forthwith with a number of leading officers who were members of the Brotherhood, particularly, Florrie O'Donoghue in Cork. He sent emissaries to Lynch in Tipperary and to Tom Hales and Tom Barry and to other leaders whom he respected. He made it clear that those who wished, would be welcome to join the National Army with commissions. Anyone who wanted to go home would be free to do so and for those who wished, he would provide arms and transport and other equipment and the IRA would be free to fight in Derry, Tyrone, Fermanagh, South Armagh and South Down. He was not aware that the British were fully cognisant of his plans, and had already formulated their own deadly riposte.

Collins' peace efforts were quite successful. He used a layer of mutually respected neutral officers and on the old Fenian principle of separate discussions with each IRA division, peace would be signed and the civil war declared over, and the Provisional Government in Dublin would be unable to start it again. This was the policy of the Free State War Council, which in reality, was acting as a de facto military Government. But the British decided to take a hand in the game and important meetings were held between Andy Cope, Tim Healy and Kevin O'Higgins. This trio decided to change the rules.

Collins did not understand the level of agreement between the leading members of the Provisional Cabinet and the British, and he misunderstood the power of MI6 to overturn the peace and destroy everything. Churchill and Lloyd-George were in daily communication with Cope, who transmitted their opinions to O'Higgins and Healy, and it would appear, for some time that these men were the real Government of Ireland. The British immediately warned that Collins was giving rifles to the IRA, that he was making peace, and no matter what would happen, the British would not tolerate this. They threatened that the Treaty would be abrogated unless the war was continued. If peace was made with the IRA, and the attempt made to call a meeting of the Parliament, to put in motion the machinery of the Collins/de Valera pact, on which the election had been fought, and which was, in fact, the legal basis of the State at the time, they would repudiate the Treaty and reoccupy Dublin. The Parliament was not summoned, the junta of O'Higgins, Healy and Cope manipulated the other gullible members of the anti-Collins, anti-IRB faction, in the interests of Britain and the Civil War.

O'Higgins and Healy discussed this in depth after receiving the final threatening message from Cope, with a few of their trusted colleagues in Government, principally McNeill and Ernest Blythe, and O'Higgins summed up the necessity of the situation by saying, that the government and the army of the country was perfectly sound, but that only one madman was leading the country into chaos and anarchy, and he quoted the words of Patrick Pearse, "One man must die for the people". To continue the civil war and avoid another British occupation, Collins must be "let die". It was agreed that arrangements be made accordingly. Cope had simultaneous and parallel communication, on a daily basis, with Emmet Dalton, and Dalton was instructed to make the necessary arrangements. It was agreed that an English finger must pull the trigger, under cover of an IRA attack, which would be provoked.

Shortly after this meeting, Cope summoned Dalton, who was his most trusted agent, and informed him that the two governments had decided that Collins was a "loose cannon" endangering the whole ship of state, and would have to be shot. Dalton was horrified and ashen-faced, unable to speak clearly, as Cope outlined the situation, and insisted on skimming through the lists of reliable ex-soldiers who had helped MI6 in the Middle East during the Great War, and were now in the Provisional Army. They settled on two soldiers then in Dublin, one in Portobello Barracks and one in Beggars Bush, Corry and Dixon.

Both of them had seen service in Mesopotamia and had been employed by MI6 on some sensitive tasks involving the shooting of a few awkward Arabs who had balked at Allenby's plans for the region. MB Corry from Rock Ferry in Cheshire, seemed the most promising. He had been an orphan, joining the army from the orphanage and was "very reliable". Dalton was initially reluctant to get involved in the liquidation of Collins, and demurred at the suggestion, stressing the dangers of the course of action. The murder of Collins, with whom he had established friendly, even affectionate relations would bring an explosion of anger throughout Ireland. Cope insisted that it could be done by blaming the IRA in the confusion of some ambush. He was angry with Dalton, reminding him of his close friendship with his patron, Sir Henry Wilson. Cope stated that he had absolute proof that Collins had ordered the shooting of Wilson, in a message to Reggie Dunne, as a reprisal for the pogroms against Catholics in Belfast. Dalton agreed that Collins bore a responsibility for the shooting of Wilson, and with a heavy heart accepted his bloody task. He realised that at that stage he had no alternative – he was then in possession of state secrets which the British Government must take any necessary steps to keep silent.

The next morning he had a meeting with the two soldiers in his office at Beggars Bush Barracks. Corry was from Chester and Dixon was a Dubliner who had served in the Connaught Rangers. Corry was a stolid, sandy-haired, unimaginative type, Dixon rather darker and more excitable. Dalton explained that there was an extremely sensitive job to be carried out on behalf of the King and the Irish Government, a necessary execution of a prominent figure. They would have to be very discreet about it, and he would see that they were well-rewarded. There would be a bounty of £10,000, and they would receive two pensions for service, one from the Irish Government and one from the UK. He would also assist them in relocating to any part of the Empire with their families, and they would be given all facilities, since he assumed that they would not wish to remain in Ireland after the completion of their task.

The two experienced assassins were not told of the identity of their intended victim, but they had heard all the gossip floating around the Free State Army about Collins' ambivalent attitude towards the IRA, and the amount of the bounty was a clear pointer. They looked at each other with excitement and anticipation, and agreed eagerly to take the orders. They were instructed to report to Dalton later in Cork, as part of the CIC's entourage. Dalton left immediately to return to his command in Cork, having taken two days leave to attend his sick mother.

The next week, Collins had arranged to go down to West Cork, to expedite peace negotiations. He had decided to set up a final meeting with Florrie O'Donoghue, Cork Head Centre, and the other neutral Republican officers who were in the IRB. A conference of the Munster IRA was also being held in West Cork. Liam Lynch would be present, and within a few miles of the same area, Eamon de Valera and Erskine Childers, on behalf of the political wing of the Republican movement would also be present. The neutral IRB officers would shuttle between the two sides and act as honest brokers in the peace endeavours. Collins was carefully stage managing the whole operation. His intention would be, that by 25 August, while still in Cork, he would formally declare the civil war over. The next day, 18 August, Emmet Dalton, O/C of Cork, radioed to Collins in Portobello regarding answers to the peace feelers, from prominent neutrals. The message in cypher was:

'1. A week's truce to be immediately arranged on the basis of the existing military position.

2. During the interval facilities to be afforded to Republican military

and political leaders to hold a meeting to discuss the making of peace on the following basis:

(a) Republican opposition to the government and parliament to be on constitutional lines.

(b) Members of the Republican forces who desire to return to civil life will be allowed to return to their occupations without molestation or penalisation.

(c) Members of the Republican forces who wish to join the National Army will be received therein with due recognition of rank and service.

(d) Arms and munitions in possession of Republican forces will be handed over to a committee to be mutually agreed upon.

(e) There will be a general amnesty for all political prisoners."

Collins replied on 19 August:

"Wireless despatch received. Will you say by cypher who the prominent citizens responsible for the offer are. Have the Irregular leaders, political and military, agreed to the offer and is it made on their behalf?

Government offer published in the press 5 June and conveyed to the Peoples Rights Association, Cork stands. For your guidance the terms are:

First: Transfer into the National Army of all war materials.

Second: Restoration, without exception, of all seized property and money.

Third: Particulars be furnished of bridges, railways, roads which are or have been mined or rendered otherwise unsafe.

Commander-in-Chief."

That evening, Collins and some officers and two members of the Cabinet attended a reception at Furry Park House, hosted by Moya and Crompton Llewelyn Davies.

The exchanges of radio messages with Dalton were known to Mulcahy, as Chief of Staff, and to O'Higgins, who was then on temporary assignment to military headquarters at Portobello, although not himself a military man. O'Higgins realised that time was running out. If Collins made peace, then the Provisional Free State Parliament must meet: the Collins/de Valera Pact would come into operation: There would be a coalition Cumann na nGaedhal/Sinn Féin cabinet, probably with Collins as President of the Executive Council: The IRB would triumph. It was the hinge of fate. There were barely two days left. He must act at once. He had an urgent conversation with Cope, who immediately sent a trusted agent to Cork to brief Dalton, and Cope also made some sinister arrangements with his agents in the Portobello Command.

The next fateful day, 19 August, Privates Dixon and Corry had leave, and walked together about Dublin, discussing the task and the great opportunity that lay before them. They agreed that there would be risks involved, but there would also be great rewards. However, they began to drink quite a lot in different parts of the city. In the afternoon, the differences of personality between them came to the fore. The more Corry drank, the quieter and more morose he became. The more Dixon drank, the more flamboyant and reckless his talk, until Corry was forced to drag him out of the pub and sit for an hour on the bench in front of the canal at Baggot St. Bridge. They began to quarrel, Dixon stating, in a thick voice, that it wouldn't be necessary for Corry to come on the job, since he was fully capable of doing it himself.

Corry, much the more cautious of the two, said that they must obey orders – the only hope of success and escape was to do precisely what they were told and depend on the support structure. Dixon blustered, and said that there was no need to wait until they went to Cork, where the Big Fellow would be amongst friends, he could be got that night in Dublin, and he, Dixon had heard that there was a platoon to go on guard duty at a party in Killester where Collins and some ministers would be, that very night.

Dixon was deaf to caution, and repeated that if he did the job, as he said, he would still give Corry some of the bounty, but not half. Corry refused to discuss the matter any further. They parted angrily, Corry heading up the canal towards Portobello, and Dixon staggering back to his billet in Beggars Bush.

Corry turned again at the corner, and watched uneasily as Dixon crossed the road. He turned to follow Dixon, imbued with a sudden dread. Sometime later, Dixon stumbled through the gate of Beggars Bush, grumbling at the challenge of the sentry, who returned his curses, but let him past. Corry stood irresolutely on the other side of the road, and gradually his fears were calmed. He was just about to turn back to his barracks, when he saw, to his absolute horror, Dixon cycling somewhat uncertainly through the Beggars Bush gate, waving casually to the guard, with a service rifle slung on his back.

Corry was rooted to the ground. Despite the rigid rule that he must not approach Cope directly, he knew that the government must be informed at all costs, and Dalton was by then well back in Cork. Corry rushed up to the phone in the guardroom at Portobello, and closing the door, he quickly phoned Cope's private office on the emergency number he had been given by Dalton. After some delay in establishing his credentials, he got through. Cope was angry and snapped the nose of him. Corry was extremely apologetic, and explained that he couldn't contact General Dalton, and there was a terrible disaster looming which the government must know about immediately. Cope requested him to come to the back entrance of his office, and he would be met there.

A half-hour later, Cope listened in stony silence while Corry gave his version of the days work with Dixon. Cope controlled his anger, and dismissed Corry, instructing him to be ready to travel to Cork the next day as arranged, and keep his silence. For a while, Cope sat with his head on his arms on his desk, pondering the dilemma. It was clear that the mad escapade would not end in the death of Collins, but Dixon must not survive to talk, since once started, he would sing like a canary. Dixon would have to be blocked and silenced, and the British and Free State Governments extricated from the mess. How best to do this? After a while, Cope wearily reached for the telephone and requested a line to Colonel Neligan at Beggars Bush. Neligan was in the mess, but quickly went to his office when told that Cope was on the phone. Cope explained that a reliable agent – Neligan nodded knowingly – had overheard a drunken soldier swear that he would shoot Mick, the Big Fellow, that night, and he had been seen leaving the barracks on a bicycle, with a rifle on his back. There might be nothing in the story, but Cope felt that Neligan should know about it.

Neligan thanked him for the information and puzzled over it for a while. Why were the British so anxious to preserve Mick whom they knew was their most effective enemy?.

He realised that the security aspect must come first and he called his personal driver and also a young lad named Bill McKenna, who was a second cousin of Neligan's wife, who had been hanging around Neligan's office for some time. He had wanted to join the Army, but was too young. But Neligan had engaged him in some odd jobs, and as a courier, since he was family, and reliable and discreet.

He instructed young McKenna to proceed to Furry Park, and to give a verbal message that a drunken and disgruntled soldier had headed in that direction, with the intention of shooting Collins. The message was to be given to a senior officer, preferably Joe O'Reilly, or Cullen. It was almost midnight when Neligan's driver pulled up at the gates of Furry Park.

That night, there was a private, but glittering party at Furry Park. Moya and Crompton had hosted a memorable gathering, including George Bernard Shaw, Sir John and Lady Hazel Lavery, Horace Plunkett, the pioneer of the co-operative movement in Ireland, Mrs Plunkett, Desmond Fitzgerald, Minister of Information in the Provisional Free State Government, and Mrs Joan Fitzgerald, parents of a future Taoiseach, Garrett Fitzgerald, Piaras Beaslai and Joe O'Reilly. Collins was the lion of the occasion, and was in ebullient form. His plans were working towards fruition, he was confident that the Civil War would be over within a few weeks, and at the first meeting of the Saorstat Dáil, the third Dáil, he would finally emerge as the President of the Irish State, no longer "virtually established" but in actual being. He could be forgiven for strutting a little, and Moya's eyes beamed approvingly.

The shadowy figures of Liam Cullen and Charley Dalton moved through the trees around the house. There was still a war going on, and Collins was the Commander-in-chief, with a certain security protocol to be observed. There was a small platoon covering the gate and the main entry to the house and two sentries at the rear. A small figure entered the gate, and was quickly challenged by Dalton.

"Name – and business?"

"Bill McKenna, I am a messenger from Colonel Neligan."

"What do you want here?"

"I have a message for General Collins"

"You will have to give it to this man – he is General Cullen and the senior officer here."

"Colonel Neligan sent me. He has information from a tout that some disgruntled British ex-soldier is coming here to shoot General Collins tonight. He is on a black bicycle, and has a rifle."

"Good lad – what age are you?"

"Fifteen Sir."

"Good lad, Bill, this night's message will be to your credit. I'll talk to Neligan about you. Go back with the driver and report to Colonel Neligan."

Inside the main drawing room, the talk was effervescent and confident. Joe O'Reilly whispered a warning to Collins, who was sitting in the bow window, with his back to the trees, chatting to Moya and questioning her and Crompton about the Balfour Declaration on Palestine, which promised a national home to the Jews, which had also been promised to the Arabs by Allenby. He almost choked on a cream bun, while trying to articulate a quip about "Perfidious Albion". Collins waved O'Reilly away. "Look after it, Joe." He refused to move from the window seat. The anguished O'Reilly, who spent a great part of his life praying for Michael Collin's welfare, stood behind him, interposing his own body between Collins and any possible sniper, to Collin's visible annoyance. Outside, Dalton and Cullen patrolled the grounds, and their vigilance was rewarded an hour later. A soldier was captured halfway up a tree, with a rifle on his back. He was quite drunk, and did not seem to realise the seriousness of his position.

Charley Dalton saw at once that there was a clear view from the tree through the main window into the great room, where behind light curtains, figures could be seen moving to and fro, and in the window itself, a familiar burly figure was to be seen, with his head close to that of a tall woman. Dalton and Cullen took the prisoner down to the end of the estate, at the sloblands on the shore, and questioned him. At first he tried to resort to a sullen silence, but Dalton was not polite nor gentle. The prisoner was reduced to moans and sobs, and then confessed that his name was George Dixon, and he was a soldier. He had a grudge, and he was hoping that General Collins would hear his case. They took him down to the shore and put a bullet through his head and rolled his body into the tide.

Back at the house, Joe O'Reilly was told how the affair had ended. He told Collins of the mysterious message and the botched attempt. Collins was intrigued by the thought of the young boy and he asked O'Reilly to arrange that the boy come next day with him on his journey to Cork. O'Reilly fixed the matter up with Neligan, and on Collin's final journey south the next day, young Bill McKenna was in the entourage. Many years later, he gave these details of that memorable night to Seamus O'Cannain, Chairman of the Furry Park Preservation Society. On 20 August, at 6 a.m., Collins left Dublin. When he came down to the parade ground in the barracks, he noticed with surprise, that his convoy arrangements had been changed. His trusted driver, Pat Swan, was no longer there, and the touring car which he was to use, had two new drivers in it. He demanded to know the reason and was told that Swan had been charged with some minor military infringement, driving while drunk, and was confined to barracks for a week. In the meantime, two other experienced drivers, Corry and Quinn, would drive him on this trip. Quinn was a Dublin man, but Corry was one of the new breed of British ex-soldiers who had joined the Provisional Army.

Collins looked at him rather dubiously, but he had to be on his way. There was a strict schedule, and Collins and his immediate friends, such as General Liam Tobin, were reassured by the look of devotion which he gave Collins when he saluted the General. However, they were not aware of the reasons why the approving smile was on Corry's face.

Corry had been drawing two salaries for a considerable time. During the War, he had been a transport driver in the Middle East, in Mesopotamia. He had also worked for MI6, and was one of their top operatives, on the "hit man" level, having been involved in a number of executions of awkward Arabs, and others who couldn't be trusted to look after British interests. He had remained in the British Army until 1921, when his extra curricular services for MI6 came to the notice of those who were recruiting for the new Provisional Government Free State Army in Dublin, and he was encouraged to join, so that he would be part of the back up staff for British operatives in Dublin.

Corry was not a complex person. As a soldier, he was quite simple minded, his job was to kill whomsoever the Kings' officers told him to kill, and he would be well paid for it. He did not have a great deal of imagination, but he intended to retire quite soon, having been told that the payment for the job he had been selected to do in Ireland, would indeed be adequate for all his needs. He would have two pensions and a bonus, and he would have a little pub on the road between Chester and Stoke-on-Trent, the scene of his childhood. He would grow roses, of which he was passionately fond, and he would explore all the stupid soft headed girls of Cheshire, who were extremely easy going in the ways of satisfying men.

So he beamed at Collins, and the convoy headed off that early morning of 20 August. The first stop was at Portlaoise to visit the prison. Collins had a long conversation with Tom Malone, a leading Republican prisoner there, in which he explored the possibilities of Malone joining his peace campaign and was encouraged by what he had heard. On leaving, he told the Governor to be very careful of Tom, and he thumped his one fist into the other and said that "the three Toms would do it for me", by which he meant Tom Barry, Tom Hales and Tom Malone. He then went on his lengthy journey through Limerick and arrived very late at night at the Imperial Hotel. There were two Free State Army sentries on duty at the main door of the hotel. Both were asleep. Collins lifted them up by the chin and crashed both their heads together.

The next day he had extensive discussions with Emmet Dalton, who was O/C of the Free State Army garrison in Cork. They made plans for a further inspection next day in the western half of the county, calling at Macroom, Bandon and meeting many members of his own family and also a number of neutral IRA and IRB officers who were party to the peace plans, and were crucial to the next phase of Collins' design. That afternoon as Collins was leaving Ballincollig barracks he noticed the sentries roughing up a civilian motorcyclist. Collins intervened, and was told that the motorcyclist was insisting on speaking to him personally. Collins demanded to know what it was about and the motorcyclist replied "I have a message from Liam Lynch for you". Both men then moved away and then had a serious conversation in private for ten minutes. It was later reported that the message from Lynch contained agreement to meet three neutral officers, who were named, provided that safe conducts were given and no military action taken for three days. West Cork was a microcosm of all the bitterness and futility of the civil war. The officer in command of the IRA there was Commandant General Tom Hales; the O/C of the Free State army was his brother Lieutenant General Sean Hales. Both were to die.

There was a web of neutral IRA officers who had given sterling service in the fight, but who refused to take up arms against their brothers, chief of whom was Florrie O'Donoghue, head centre of the IRB in Cork. These neutral officers now became busy as facilitators of peace, moving carefully between the combatants in their endeavours.

In the morning, Collins and Dalton left early and passed through Béal na Bláth and then up to Macroom and made a number of calls. At the time it appeared as if all Ireland's political and military future was concentrated upon this small part of West Cork. De Valera and Erskine Childers were there, churning out closely reasoned Republican journals which nobody was reading. There was a major conference taking place with Liam Lynch, General Tom Hales and the main officers of the 1st Southern Division. In addition, in a small village called Béal na Bláth, there was a separate conference of the 2nd West Cork Brigade and unfortunately, this was the ground for a tremendous and lethal misunderstanding.

The divisional conference attended by de Valera and by Liam Lynch discussed the general strategy of the Republican movement. They decided that the divisions were no longer practical as an organisational structure for the army fighting a guerrilla war, and that henceforth, each brigade would operate on its own, selecting its own targets and carrying out it's own operations without reference back to Divisional Headquarters.

The Cork No. 2 Brigade Staff then left the general meeting of divisional officers and proceeded to their own brigade conference in Béal na Bláth. Lynch and the other divisional officers and de Valera and Childers then proceeded to discuss the question of possible peace terms, and this took quite a long time. The entire progress of the war was also considered, which was an acrimonious operation. They finally agreed, without commitment, to listen to Collins' proposals, through the good offices of trusted neutral IRB members, and to prepare their own counter proposals for a peace programme, and in the interim to recommend scaling down all but defensive military actions.

In the meantime, the Brigade staff were having their own meeting, following upon the first decision that had been made, and they were not aware of the decision to open discussions with Collins. The next morning, when they saw the Free State troops in convoy through Béal na Bláth, they regarded this as a coat trailing exercise in search of Liam Lynch, and in pursuance of the decision of the previous day, they decided to set up an ambush, in case the convoy came back the same way that evening. This was a tragic and fateful decision. The Brigade staff were unaware of Collins' presence in the return convoy, although he had been recognised in the morning, and of the peace feelers and the possible nearing end of the War.

TWENTY

The Mouth of Blossoms

"Tho it break my heart to hear, say again the bitter words
From Derry, 'gainst Cromwell, he marched to measure swords
But the weapon of the Saxon met him on the way
And he died, at Cloc Uachtar, upon St Leonards day."

Owen Roe O'Neill

Dusk was closing in as they drove along the road from Bandon to Béal na Bláth. As Lieutenant Smith, on the motorcycle, turned the corner opposite the public house to Béal na Bláth, he noticed a cart drawn across the road, blocking the road, and two men scurrying backwards from it. At that moment a shot rang out from the lookout post down the hill. Smith quickly wheeled his motorcycle into the ditch. The Crossley tender stopped 20 or 30 yards behind. The touring car containing Collins and Dalton drew up a further 50 yards behind on the bend in the road. Hearing the shot, Dalton shouted to the driver to stop. Collins looked at him in surprise. The driver pulled into the side of the road and they all jumped out. The armoured car stopped about 30 yards behind Collins' car. Collins drew his Mauser pistol and went forward. He threw himself behind the ditch and started firing towards the crest of the hill from whence flashes of gunfire were visible. There were five IRA men on the brow of the hill and rifle fire from them began to patter on the road and against the turret of the armoured car. The machine gun on the armoured car began to fire back at them in reply. Dalton took up a position kneeling behind the bonnet of the touring Leyland car and started firing with his rifle. At this stage, the driver, Corry, had taken up a position about six feet from Collins on his right hand side and was firing from his own rifle. As he passed Dalton, he had taken Dalton's Mauser from its holster and jammed into his own pocket. Dalton paid no attention, gazing stonily ahead.

For a moment there was a lull in the firing from the machine gun in the armoured car turret. Dalton looked around with annoyance at the second driver, Quinn, who was at the rear of the car firing. "Get down there, Quinn, and tell that bastard to put another belt in." Quinn ran stooping, down the road in the protection of the hedge towards the armoured car. Dusk was falling fast and it was difficult to perceive what exactly was happening. But for a moment, at the focal point of the ambush, there was only three men, Collins, Dalton

144

and Corry. Commandant O'Connell was about 20 yards further down, lying in the hedge, firing with a rifle. Collins finished emptying his Mauser pistol at the distant figures who could be seen on the darkening skyline as they retreated up the laneway.

"There they go. Emmet, bring me a rifle." he shouted. At that moment, it was clear to Corry that his gun was empty and that for a few seconds he was unarmed. Corry was holding his rifle loosely in his left hand; in his right hand was Dalton's Mauser pistol pointed at Collins' head from a distance of about three feet. For a fraction of a second there was amazed incomprehension and anger on Collins' face and then he roared out "You bastard." just as Corry's pistol fired. The single crack of the Mauser was lost in the general confusion of the battle. Corry tossed the pistol on the roadside edge, and throwing his rifle into the firing position, he began to fire, working the bolt furiously.

Commandant O'Connell came rushing up. Dalton was leaning against the bonnet of the Leyland car, his face sick and strained. There was a rifle in his nerveless hand. He seemed incapable of speech. O'Connell asked where was Collins:

"I, think I heard him firing a moment ago."

Just then Corry appeared around the nose of the car, "I think the General is hurt, Sir?"

They rushed up the road in the gathering gloom. A few yards further on O'Connell stopped with a gasp of anger and dismay. Collins was lying at his feet, a small, neat bullet hole through his right forehead where the Mauser bullet had entered just above the hairline. An enormous gaping wound was at the back of his head, below the left ear. A large portion of his skull had been blown out, the bullet having somersaulted inside and carried out a large portion of his brain matter which was scattered profusely across the road. O'Connell knelt down beside the General and took his hand. For a moment the great big eyes looked up at him. Dalton stood beside them with a rifle in his hand, making futile gestures to fire but unable to pull the bolt. Collins was still alive, but barely. He looked with recognition at O'Connell, who took his hand and started to recite an Act of Contrition into the dying man's ear. Collins pressed firmly with his hand, then the great eyes closed and Michael Collins was dead.

He was not quite 32 – the same age as Alexander when he died at Babylon.

A young girl from the village of Beal Na Blath found Collins cap on the side of the road, at the spot where he had fallen. On the advice of a priest she brought the cap to a Free State military post in Bandon, and gave it to the Lieutenant in charge. He gave it to General Sean Hales, OC of the Free State army in Bandon. Hales noticed that there was a single small bullet hole through the front right hand side of the cap band.

Hales was deeply affected by the death of his friend and commander, and the cap aroused his suspicions and caused him to start probing into the circumstances surrounding Collins" death. He demanded an inquest and an official military inquiry, and sent the cap to GHQ in Dublin as evidence of his suspicions. The cap disappeared, but Hales continued in his campaign to find the truth. It was to lead to Dalton's resignation from the Army and Hales' own death. Early on the morning after the ambush, Collins' empty Mauser pistol was found at the ambush site, and a few hours later a local man named Tom Foley found a second Mauser after a brief search of the ditch. The second pistol had four bullets in the magazine and the initials ED were engraved on the walnut butt. This find became widely known and the next day a patrol of Free State soldiers called to Foley's house and ordered him to hand over the guns. They were never again to surface.

The Free State Government was in total disarray when the news reached Dublin that Collins was dead. There was an immediate and immense outpouring of national grief and the Government consulted the ubiquitous Cope for advice. He, mindful of the precedent of the funeral of O'Donovan Rossa in awakening Republican spirit, advised that the body of Collins be taken discreetly to Dublin by ship, avoiding the rallies and delays in every village that the funeral would involve. Mulcahy issued a calming declaration:

> "Stand calmly by your posts. Bend bravely and undaunted to your work. Let no cruel act of reprisal blemish your bright honour. Every dark hour that Michael Collins met since 1916 served but to steel the bright strength of him and temper his gay bravery. You are each left inheritors of that strength and that bravery. To each of you, falls his unfinished work. No darkness in this hour – no loss of comrades will daunt you at it. Ireland! The Army serves - strengthened by its sorrow."

Collins' beloved enemy, Tom Barry, then a Republican prisoner in Kilmainham Prison, has left a vivid picture of the reaction of the senior Republican officers to the news of the death of the commander of the army they were fighting in a bitter civil war:

> "I was talking with some other prisoners on the night of August 22nd, when the news came in that Michael Collins had been shot dead in West Cork. There was a heavy silence throughout the jail, and ten minutes later from the corridor outside the top tier of cells I looked down on the extraordinary spectacle of about a thousand kneeling Republican prisoners spontaneously reciting the Rosary aloud for the repose of the soul of the dead Michael Collins. . . . I have yet to learn of a better tribute to the part played by any man in the struggle with the English for Irish independence."

Collins' body was taken by ship, the *Classic*, to the North Wall in Dublin. It was embalmed by Oliver St. John Gogarty, whose diary, withheld for 40 years, mentioned the filling of a small hole in Collins' forehead, the entry hole of the Mauser 7.6mm Mauser bullet, with a waxy substance, and bandaging the massive exit wound.

Many thousands poured into the City Hall, and filed past the catafalque. The mourners included a distraught and sobbing Moya Llewellyn Davies, Lady Hazel Lavery, Kitty Kiernan, and a host of political and military figures. Nearly 300,000 people lined the streets of Dublin for the final journey to Glasnevin Cemetery.

John Feehan has said that Michael Collins was the greatest Irish leader since Brian Boru, but I would go further back and hold that the Irish have not had a war leader his equal – in his accomplishments – since Niall of the Nine Hostages, who marched on Rome. The national position was advanced further by him than by any other before or since, and it has receded and diminished since his death. The general population of the South has drifted an ocean away from Collins' vision and perception in 1922.

Corry, in shooting Collins, had no appreciation or responsibility for the calamities that ensued in Ireland. He was merely the agent of a malignant Fate, like the anonymous trooper who smashed Rosa Luxemburg's skull with his rifle butt. "Blind Hodur, killing the Hope of the Gods". But, who was Loki, the evil counsellor, the Iago of the Irish Revolution, who fomented disaster and loaded the assassin's gun?

A fortnight later, a most extraordinary advertisement appeared in the *Cork Examiner*, signed by Emmet Dalton, O/C of the army in Cork, to the effect that he prohibited the holding of any inquest within the county of Cork. Collins had been buried with enormous and proper ceremonial, and shortly after, the Provisional Government met and confirmed Cosgrave as President of the Executive Council of the Irish Free State. Mulcahy was Minister for Defence and Commander in Chief of the Army, and the most important person in the Government was, undoubtedly, Kevin O'Higgins, Minister for Home Affairs, who set about the establishment of the Garda Síochána throughout the country, with Michael Staines briefly as first Commissioner. Staines had been a close friend of Collins and a fellow internee in Frongoch.

Despite the oddities in O'Higgins' background, during this period he laboured well and did sterling work for the country. He and Staines had the enormous common sense to establish the Garda Síochána as an unarmed police force, whose objective was to serve the civilian population, and as far as possible, not be involved in the conflict with the Republicans which O'Higgins regarded as work for the Army. He is also widely credited with establishing the concept of the "holy Hour", whereby every public house in the country had to close from 2.30–3.30 in the afternoon, and all on the premises must leave. It was said that this was because of his own early years when it was his habit and some of his friends, to stay in a public house all day.

But O'Higgins had a virulent hatred of the IRB, which emotion he controlled until he was able to strike an effective blow. The mopping up operations continued throughout the country, with occasional skirmishes between the IRA, who were now called the "Irregulars", and the Free State Army, who called themselves the National Army. The Provisional Parliament gave extremely draconian powers to Mulcahy and the Defence Council whereby sentence of death could be passed on anyone found with arms or captured in arms. The most illustrious victim of this was, in fact, Erskine Childers.

He had given tremendous service to the movement for liberation, he had imported the arms originally to arm the Volunteers, on his yacht, the Asgard, in Howth in 1913, and then believing in the causes of small nations in the Great War, he joined the British Army and served for four years. However, when he returned home, he joined Sinn Féin and became a dedicated Republican. He had served in the Propaganda Department and was one of the secretaries to Michael Collins and the Treaty deputation. Shortly after the death of Collins, he was caught turning out his Republican press reports. Unfortunately, he was carrying a small pearl-handled revolver at the time, which was a personal present from Michael Collins, as a token of his esteem. To prepare public opinion, the Defence Council and Mulcahy first took four young prisoners who had been caught after an ambush, and announced very briefly that they had been executed in Mountjoy.

There was a storm of protest. Defending their actions in the Dáil, O'Higgins, Mulcahy and Cosgrave said that these men were picked out in the hope of ending the fight, and that they were deliberately chosen, because if they had picked out a senior leader or a Englishman, people would have thought that there was political bias behind the execution. It was quite a deliberate pointer to Erskine Childers, and a week later Childers was executed by Collins' army for possession of a small personal revolver given to him by Collins, as a gift, in the days when they were comrades-in-arms.

There was a tremendous deal of unrest in the Army around this time. The official story of Collins' shooting was not accepted by any of the experienced officers, and Emmet Dalton found it quite impossible to exercise his command. He was the butt of open insults. Every time he went into an officers mess in the evening, someone would shout "Who killed Collins?". Eventually his nerve broke, he resigned from the army and threw himself on the mercy of O'Higgins and Cosgrave. He presented a sensitive problem. It was important to make sure that he had as little contact as possible with Mulcahy, who would have him shot immediately if he suspected that Dalton had anything to do with the death of Collins. Mulcahy was aware of the army gossip, but did not give it any credence. Dalton was given a sinecure as clerk of the Senate, but his drinking and bouts of paranoia continued and eventually it was thought safer to have him go to England and have him make a new life for himself. Of course, once in England, he was given a reasonably steady job in MI6, and eventually became a photographer. His daughter, Audrey became a minor film star.

Dalton's removal did not satisfy or stifle the growing complaints in the army about the mystery of Collins' death, nor did Mulcahy's quite genuine attempt to commemorate the dead leader. The cap badge and the belt badge, of the Free State Army at the time had a brass buckle with the entwined letters of "F.F.", for Fianna Fáil, the "Army of Destiny". Mulcahy decreed that henceforth this badge would be enamelled black in mourning for Michael Collins. This was a healing political gesture.

But the great cover-up was total: there was no inquest, no enquiry or investigation of any sort; and it was almost a year later before the contrived, awkward and contradictory account of the ambush by Dalton was published in the press. Later the more forthright accounts of the ambush by M.B. Corry, the assassin, was published, with several direct contradictions of Dalton's account.

However, the general in whose area the killing had taken place, Sean Hales, who was also O/C in West Cork for the National Army, and a deputy in the Dáil, was quite unsatisfied. He demanded a full military inquiry and an inquest. It was extraordinary that this was not carried out for the death of the Commander in Chief of the Army. Hales was not to be put off. A close friend and former colleague in the IRB, Padraig O'Maille, had been elected as leas ceann comhairle or deputy speaker of the Dáil. On 6 December, Hales travelled to Dublin to discuss the question of Collins' death with O'Maille prior to the opening of the Dáil the following day. They discussed how Hales' suspicions could be raised and agreed that Dáil Éireann should establish an enquiry, regardless of the Army or the Government, and this was to be moved the next day. There is no doubt whatever that the Dáil would have accepted this motion, and that there would have been an official enquiry by officers appointed by the Dáil. That enquiry would have gradually peeled back the layers of contradictions and mysteries surrounding the death of Collins. There would have been a proper inquest with medical evidence from Dr Oliver St John Gogarty, which would have proved that Collins was shot with a 7.62mm pistol, not a .303 rifle as used by all the ambush squad.

O'Maille agreed to call General Hales to address the Dáil on behalf of the Cork Command the next day, and to accept a motion for an investigation. No one in the army or in the Council of Defence, knew that General Hales and the deputy speaker had decided on this step, but it was widely known that that they were close friends and suspected that Collins' death had been murder. Hales had bombarded GHQ with demands for an enquiry and was extremely unpopular in the top echelons of the Free State. Hales had sent an angry but indiscreet telegram, through Army wireless to O'Maille two days before coming to Dublin, outlining his proposal for a separate Dáil enquiry, and this would have quickly circulated to O'Higgins, Cope and other interested parties. When Hales arrived at the main barracks, Portobello Barracks, his driver was arrested on some trumped-up charge and he was told that there was no room for him in the barracks and that he would have to stay in a hotel that night. This was an extraordinary and disturbing way to treat a General in the Army in the middle of a civil war.

Hales met Padraig O'Maille in the Ormond Hotel that night. The next morning they left the hotel early to go to the Dáil. As they climbed onto a jaunting car just outside the hotel, there was a sudden fusillade of shots. Hales died almost immediately. There was a British lorry and some civilians in the street but no evidence of anyone else. A British officer said that they had seen two men rushing up with handguns and shooting Hales and O'Maille but there was no evidence whatever of this. The two officers concerned did not give evidence at the inquest.

O'Maille was taken to hospital and fully recovered in a few months. He was a man of great stature and enormous health and vitality. He had been in Frongoch with Michael Collins and revered the dead leader. He was a staunch member of the Brotherhood, and was a noted and greatly respected worker for the Irish language. The attack on O'Maille was a great shock. The Free State ministers immediately blamed the assassination on the bemused IRA, who knew nothing about it for several hours.

When the Dáil heard the news that morning, there was consternation. The Parliament adjourned. The Council of Defence decided that there was a grave danger that deputies would be affected by fear and would not support the Government's activities in prosecuting the civil war. However, there was no evidence as to who shot Hales and O'Maille. The IRA issued a statement saying that it had nothing to do with it, and in later years, Maurice Twomey, Sean MacBride and a number of other people, including Oscar Traynor, who had been head of the IRA in Dublin at the time, were adamant that it was not an IRA operation. A statement, purporting to be from Liam Lynch and mentioning that the Dublin Unit had made an attack and shot two deputies, was found a year and a half later. But Lynch had been in Tipperary and had no knowledge or responsibility for any action in Dublin at the time, and the provenance of this statement "discovered" after Lynch's death is highly suspect. The only groups to have profited from the death of Hales and the wounding of O'Maille were MI6 and the Free State Government, who would have been destroyed by an impartial enquiry into the death of Michael Collins.

As portrayed in the day's newspapers, a random IRA attack had taken the lives of two prominent Free State officials. A wave of fear swept through the deputies of the Third Dáil, and the pending legislation to curb the IRA seemed to be in danger. That evening, the Council of Defence met and Mulcahy decided upon a frightful reprisal against the IRA. The Cabinet were quite horrified at what Mulcahy said were the demands of the Council of Defence, that the four senior divisional commanders of the IRA, Rory O'Connor, Dick Barrett, Liam Mellowes and Joe McKelvey, who were in prison since the fall of the Four Courts, should be shot the next morning.

It is difficult to find the truth of what actually took place at that Cabinet meeting, because many contradictory rumours had been spread. There is consensus that Eoin MacNeill and Ernest Blythe agreed immediately, almost enthusiastically, and that the other members of the Cabinet fell into line. It is also accepted that O'Higgins was extremely reluctant to go along with this policy, believing that it would lead to more dangers and more deaths, and he was particularly moved at the intention to kill Rory O'Connor, who had been a close friend of his, and had been best man at his wedding. Eventually, he agreed. The last to agree was Joe McGrath who came late to the meeting and was told that the cabinet was then unanimous. It was a cowardly and murderous decision, poisoning political discussion for a generation, and having particularly wounding effects in the North.

The next morning, as dawn broke over Mountjoy, the four men were taken out and shot. The killing was done very inefficiently, the firing squads were nervous and unsure of themselves. While it seemed that O'Connor, Mellowes and Barrett got reasonably quick deaths, Joe McKelvey, head of the Fourth Northern Division and Assistant Chief of Staff of the IRA, died crying in agony for a final bullet.

TWENTY-ONE

A Carnival of Reaction

Following the executions in Mountjoy Prison, the civil war took an increasingly vicious turn. It seemed that the civilian Government, had taken a back seat, and control was entirely in the hands of O'Higgins, Mulcahy, McMahon and Eoin O'Duffy. They seemed almost fanatically determined to escape from their past when they had been senior officers in the Brotherhood. A campaign of indiscriminate murder was carried out by the Government forces, and it appeared as if the Council for Defence, under Mulcahy, was determined to make sure that all the senior officers of the Free State Army had blood on their hands. In every command, senior Republican prisoners were taken out, and in some cases were shot the next morning after a drumhead court martial. A total of 77 official executions were carried out. All should have been given the protection of the Geneva Convention but it had the desired effect of ensuring that the senior military officers were tightly bound to the new State.

At the same time, the IRB seemed to be losing a large part of its influence, and members of the IRB found themselves increasing isolated within the Free State Army Command as ex-British soldiers and people who had not been active in the War of Independence, were promoted and given senior responsibilities over the heads of those who had been the original Free State cadres. On the other side in the civil war, a severe blow was struck to the remnants of the IRB and the Republican movement when Liam Lynch was shot on 10 April 1923.

Meanwhile, there was unrest and dissatisfaction developing in the ranks of the Free State Army. Following the death of Michael Collins, Liam Tobin, Thornton, Cullen and Charlie Dalton and other close associates of Collins during the Tan War period founded an association called "The IRA Association". It was a new secret society composed almost entirely of members of the IRB and was organised on the same lines. Its objective was to maintain the original principles and objectives of Collins and of the IRB, and its declared purpose was to ensure that the Treaty was to be used as Collins had promised, as a stepping stone to the Republic. Tentative efforts were made to make contact with members of the IRB on the Republican side, with the intention of bringing about a ceasefire. There was some talking, but conditions were very difficult, and distrust was rife.

In May 1923, Michael Brennan, the officer commanding Limerick wrote to Mulcahy, stating that he and other senior officers were worried by prospect of finding that the Free State was the end for which they fought, not the means to that end. This feeling was very widespread throughout the National Army. Men were annoyed by the presence of many new soldiers in the ranks with no previous experience and by the promotion of ex-British officers, who had fought against them a few years before. They were also worried by the personal and political divisions of the Free State Cabinet and by the relationship of the Army to the civil power. The principal concern of the leaders of the Free State Army was to develop an efficient disciplined army responsive to the wishes of the Government but they realised that many senior officers with excellent records, were not being retained in their commands, while British officers were replacing them. These tensions came to a head and finally erupted with the obvious defeat of the Republican Movement. At the end of 1923, Frank Aitken, Chief of Staff of the IRA still in the field, called upon the scattered and beaten Republican forces to dump their arms and return to their homes. The tragic, stupid and unnecessary Civil War was technically over, eighteen months too late.

In February 1924, Mulcahy issued Staff Memorandum No 12, which demoted or dismissed almost every member of the IRA organisation, and made it clear that former members of the IRB were not going to be retained in the Army. It was obviously the intention to establish an entirely new Army based upon personal support for members of the Cabinet, and what they would have regarded as politically more responsible ex-British officers, who had joined in large numbers after the Truce.

The issue of this memorandum sparked off what has been called the "Free State Army Mutiny". The mutiny officially began on 6 March 1924, but was a very low key affair. Liam Tobin and Charlie Dalton presented an ultimatum to the Cosgrave Government demanding changes in the Army, and expressed dissatisfaction with the direction the Free State had taken since the Treaty. The officers declared that they and the people had accepted the Treaty only as a stepping stone to the Republic, and the Government had betrayed this ideal. They demanded that the Government meet them to discuss their interpretation of the Treaty and they set their formal conditions; the removal and replacement of the Army Council and immediate suspension of de-mobilisation and reorganisation. They threatened that if the Government did not comply with their demands,

> "We would take such action as to make clear to the Irish people that they were not renegades or traitors to the ideals and interests and to accept the Treaty. Our organisation fully realises the seriousness of the actions we may be compelled to take, but we can no longer be party to the treachery that threatens to destroy the aspirations of the Nation."

This was clearly seen as a threat of an imminent *coup d'etat*. There was a sympathetic response from many other Free State officers throughout the country; 49 officers resigned, including three major generals, five colonels, 17 commandants and 12 captains. Fifty officers left their barracks with war materials, including Lewis machineguns. Chief of Staff, Sean McMahon, feared that unless steps were taken at once, the army would develop into an armed mob. Wild rumours swept the Free State Establishment, of talks and conspiracies between the "army mutineers" and the beaten remnants of the IRA, and of a revival of the Irish Republican Brotherhood.

The Executive Council, therefore, ordered the arrest of the two signatories, Tobin and Dalton. The military party visited several houses in Dublin, including that of Joe McGrath, the Minister of Industry and Commerce. McGrath, a sturdy, independent spirit, explained his reasons. He refused to be party to the start of a blaze, which he believed would have consumed the country. He would not be party to taking action against a body of men who were responsible, very largely, for the birth of the Free State. Mulcahy, as Minister of Defence, released a statement to the press on 10 March 1924,

> "Two Army Officers have attempted to arouse the Army in a challenge to the authority of the Government. This is an outrageous departure from the spirit of the Army and it will not be tolerated."

The Government decided, at this moment of crisis, to appoint a new commander of the National Army in place of General Sean McMahon, whom they did not trust as he was a member of the IRB. General Eoin O'Duffy, Commandant of the Civil Guard, who had formerly been a general officer of the Army, was appointed to the new position as General Officer Commanding the Defence Forces, and Cosgrave explained in the Dáil that the new appointment was intended to strengthen in the Headquarter staff as part of the Cabinet's plans to deal with the mutiny. However, it was probably more due to the fact that they did not entirely trust Mulcahy and the other Army GHQ members. Mulcahy, of course, resented the appointment of O'Duffy, characterising him as an outsider who was out of touch with the military.

Apparently, the Government did not at this time know that O'Duffy, himself, was still a senior member of the IRB. Cumann na nGaedhal, the government party, held an important Party meeting to evaluate policy towards the mutineers. The meeting lasted for six hours, and Joe McGrath was the star performer. Mulcahy was present at the meeting, of course, but did not take any part. He realised that the sands were shifting under the Government. At the meeting, McGrath claimed that the mutiny was not a mutiny at all, but a dispute between two rebel organisations, the Old IRA and the IRB. He charged that their staff wanted to reorganise the Brotherhood and they were in exactly the same category as the rebellious officers, Major General Tobin and Colonel Dalton, who did the same. McGrath described his role as a bridge between the two groups, claiming that he tried to bring the leaders of the Old IRA and the IRB together, but failed. There was a lengthy debate on the role of secret societies in the army, and O'Higgins was reinforced in his determination that at all costs he must smash the IRB and get rid of all its members from the

Government.

The Government decided to proceed and charge all the mutinous officers, and the Adjutant General Gearóid O'Sullivan, himself a "Brother", sent out the following orders to command officers:

> "In connection with the recent mutinous actions of certain officers of the National Forces, General Officers Commanding will ensure that action is taken as follows: Every person charged with an offence arising out of the recent attempted mutiny, will be placed under arrest and charged accordingly, and every such arrest will be immediately notified by wireless to the Adjutant General."

Mulcahy had received information that a meeting of mutinous officers was being held in Devlin's public house in Parnell Street, one of Michael Collins' old meeting houses. Immediate arrangements were made to have the house surrounded and all the members arrested. On arrival, the troops discovered that a number of armed mutineers were inside; they decided they had no authority to raid the house and informed the officers that they would be arrested as soon as they came out. The mutineers barricaded the stairs and were prepared to fight. In the meantime, most of the officers had escaped across the rooftops and only eleven officers were arrested. This was the farcical end of the comic opera mutiny. Michael Collins must have been turning in his grave.

O'Higgins judged that the time was right to strike at the remnants of the IRB, and accordingly the Cabinet decided to ask for the resignation of the Chief of Staff, the Adjutant General, the Quartermaster General and that Mulcahy be removed from his office as Minister of Defence and be replaced by General O'Duffy in complete command of the Army. Mulcahy did not know at that moment that he was being sacked. When he heard about it a few hours later, he immediately resigned. Twenty eight years were to pass before he again sat in an Irish Cabinet.

Gearoid O'Sullivan and Sean O'Muirthuile also resigned from the posts of Adjutant General and Quartermaster General. Chief of Staff McMahon refused to resign and he was dismissed. There was almost a complete clearing out of all the surviving members of the IRB in the Free State apparatus; and of all officers who had shown any sympathy to the ideals of Michael Collins.

Richard Mulcahy was bitterly attacked in the Dáil, and it would seem in retrospect, that a hidden hand had been in operation in the upper ranks of the movement for several years; that in the discussions about the Treaty, influences were brought to bear and decisions were made that were not in the interests of the Nation; that on many occasions when it would have been possible to heal the split and make peace, passions and tempers were deliberately inflamed, and that successive layers of Republicanism and of the IRB within the Government and the Free State Army, and within the Sinn Fein Party, were successfully pushed out, and then those who pushed them out, themselves fell victim to the same process. Eventually, by 1925, a tiny handful of cunning people, O'Higgins and two or three others, who had started the War with no influence, no position, no powerful allies, except the British establishment, were ensconced as titular leaders and the Government of the Irish Free State.

The Civil War was over, the mutiny was over and nothing but the grey pall of Free State conservatism overspread the nation. There was no role in the new State for the Irish Republican Brotherhood, and finally, recognising that fact, Sean O'Muirthuile and seven or eight others met in the Secretary's Lodge in the Phoenix Park to wind up the IRB. All of them had been previously powerful officers and members of the Government. They all left that meeting as private citizens with no influence. The Free State branch of the IRB was formally wound up, and their total funds amounting to £3,800 were given to two members of the Council for safekeeping and charitable work. Sean O'Muirthuile was given £2,000 to pay outstanding debts and to write a history of the IRB.

O'Muirthuile's history was never distributed. The printing plates were seized and smashed by order of the Free State Government, and it is very difficult to get authentic transcripts of the manuscript. On the other side, the Republican wing of the IRB was terminated by the IRA Executive in January 1924, and this termination was formally reported to Frank Aiken, Chief of Staff.

It is important to note that by the time of these actions to end the IRB, the remnants of the Brotherhood had come to be parallel to the opposing military factions of the IRA and the Free State Army. The death of Michael Collins ended any possibility of the Brotherhood surviving and enjoying autonomy in operating as an independent political organisation within the Free State, but instead it had become a creature of the structures that had been invented, built up and controlled by it. It was a classic example of the Revolution eating its own children.

On the Free State side, the IRB had been directed informally, for a short time, as an instrument of Government policy. On the Republican side, the IRA Executive exercised complete control of its IRB members, in a reversal of Collins' intent. The organisation had become the servant, and not the master, of the military forces in the country. So ended the Irish Republican Brotherhood, an extraordinarily tenacious and powerful secret society that had achieved so much. It had existed over two lifetimes and had created the modern Ireland against great odds. It ended with its task still incomplete: it had won the war but lost the peace.

TWENTY-TWO

Epilogues

Kevin O'Higgins

One of the future important candidates selected to contest the 1918 General Election by Collins and Boland was a young man from Offaly, Kevin O'Higgins. His mother was a daughter of T.D. Sullivan, a former Lord Mayor of Dublin and owner of the newspaper *The Nation*. She was also a sister-in-law of Tim Healy, and the entire O'Higgins family had a constitutional nationalist background, Redmondite, and very anti-republican. However, Boland did not research the background carefully enough and he and Collins were not aware of O'Higgins' family connections and background when they selected him to stand for Dáil Éireann, a disastrous decision which altered history. He was one of the few who slipped through the selection criteria of IRB membership or previous Volunteer activities

O'Higgins was an unusual character. Originally intended for the priesthood, he was expelled from Maynooth Seminary for breaches of discipline, and was later again expelled from Carlow Seminary, when given a second chance. He then joined the Volunteers, briefly, but did not take part in the Rising. He was returned unopposed as Sinn Féin member for Queens' County in the 1918 election, and became assistant to W.T. Cosgrave, Minister for Local Government in the first Dáil, thus commencing and cementing the familiar alliance between the families of the Healy, O'Higgins, Cosgrave, and MacNeill families that was such a feature of the fledgling Irish Free State, and which epitomised the social and ethical character of the period.

O'Higgins took no active part in the Anglo-Irish War. He continued his law studies, and his Dáil duties were very light as the Dáil rarely met. He came rapidly to the fore after the Truce, and became a leading member of the Provisional Free State Government. He was a frequent visitor to London, and rapidly established a rapport with Winston Churchill. At a time when Sir Henry Wilson was indiscreetly demanding the return of British troops to the streets of Dublin, Churchill wrote in the *Times* that there was no need: "A man in these counties (26) arises, who will crush murder and anarchy, and restore Law and Order." O'Higgins was noted for his hatred of the IRB throughout the period from 1919 to 1922, and in the end, he triumphed over it. He was murdered near his home in Booterstown, on 10 July 1927.

The Sunday morning was bright and cold as Kevin O'Higgins left his house at Cross Avenue, firmly reproving his detective who had wanted to accompany him. He was going to walk down as far as the shore by Booterstown Station before coming back for Mass. He wanted to be alone to think.

As he walked down Cross Avenue and turned towards the distant blue shimmering sea, his mind was engaged in a swift review of the past five years since the death of Collins. So much had been accomplished. Now there were glittering prospects open. He was about to stride forth on a large stage, not just Ireland, not even the Empire. Confident of his own abilities, he was sure that as the acknowledged leader of Ireland he would make his mark. With the springboard of the Free State under his feet, there was no doubt that the next decade would see Ireland become a major world nation of importance and influence.

He thought of all the men who had stood in his path, de Valera, a man totally without political talent or future, hidebound by his own theories. Mulcahy, limited, but a good man, a good staff officer, pity he was so stiff, and then there was Collins, the only one who was his equal. It was a pity he had to go, but it was necessary. He thought again of the phrase he had used from a play of Pearse; "One man must die for the people". Mick was too extravagant. No balance. His mind flitted briefly to the "Seventy Seven". What a pity. He took some comfort from the thought that it was mainly Mulcahy's doing – he never felt really at ease with that man in the Cabinet. Mulcahy would drink blood – poacher turned gamekeeper. He was really and truly sorry about Rory.

Suddenly his thoughts were interrupted. A shadow fell across him. There were three men standing in front of him very close. With an icy shock of surprise he recognised them. Two of them, he knew, had been members of Collins's old Squad, his Praetorian Guard, he called them, during the Tan War. Coughlan and Gannon. Yes, Bill Gannon, and Tim Coughlan. The third was vague and indeterminate, yes, Archie Doyle. He had been in the last Active Service Unit in the Dublin Brigade.

They all held revolvers. O'Higgins stretched out his left hand, almost as if in appeal just as the guns fired. The impact threw him against the wall and he slid down on to the pavement. In an instant a tremendous change occurred. His superb, ordered governing brain went into overdrive. Looking on his fate, many times faster than normal thought, his intellect reviewed the situation, assessed it. He came to certain conclusions.

Suddenly, all his ambitions, his burning pride, his past, political thought, the future before him as a leader of the country were of no importance now. He was dying and he knew it. How best could that time be used?

Time seemed to spin very slowly as he thought. He was not an overly pious Catholic, he accepted religion because it was unthinkable to go against it and the people who believed in it. But within the tenets of his religion he realised that the most important thing of all, now that he was dying, was that he must forgive his enemies, if only for the sake of his own immortal soul. His eyes were still open, he stretched out his hands towards Bill Gannon.

"Bill, Bill, listen to me."

His voice was choked. The three men gazed at him, prepared to fire again, but it was clearly not necessary. Gannon leaned forward in answer to the entreaty and the beckoning arm.

"Bill, forget it all. I forgive you. Let this be the last of the killings. No reprisals, no more killing."

For a moment his three killers gazed uncomprehendingly, then turned swiftly and ran down the street towards the waiting car.

Kevin O'Higgins lived for several hours. He was taken to his own house and died surrounded by his wife and family and many of his colleagues in the Government, the doctor having seen at once that it was futile to take him to a hospital. He was made as comfortable as possible and dictated his will to a solicitor. He made provisions for his children and his wife and many messages to his associates in Government. Despite immense pressure, he did not indicate who had killed him, although it was suspected that he knew. He said several times: "Let this be the end of the killings. No reprisals, no reprisals." It was late that evening when he closed his eyes for the last time. He had just joked with his wife about sitting on a damp cloud, playing a harp, and arguing politics with Mick. He had made MacNeill pledge that there would be no reprisals, no vengeance. In all his crowded life, nothing became him like his leaving of it.

De Valera and Fianna Fáil

In 1925, de Valera failed in an attempt to persuade Sinn Féin to take the oath and enter the Dáil. He withdrew from Sinn Féin and formed his own political organisation, together with the leading members of Sinn Féin and the ex-members of the IRB, and the old IRA, people like Sean T. O'Kelly, Sean Lamass, Oscar Traynor, Frank Aiken, and others. De Valera led his party into the Dáil and took the Oath of Allegiance, which he had split the Republican movement over five years before. Questioned how he could square this action with his previous policy he replied "I did not really take an oath. My fingers did not touch the Bible". The new party was called Fianna Fáil.

The economic situation in the country deteriorated for the next six years. With the single exception of the Shannon Hydro-Electric scheme, no economic initiative of any consequence was taken by Cumann na nGaedhal, a party and a government seemingly without talent or initiative. Then came the depression of 1932. With the collapse of capitalism throughout the world, and enormous new changes. Roosevelt came to power in the US, with the "New Deal". The repercussions of this economic collapse brought Fianna Fáil to power, with the help of the Labour Party, after a general election in 1932. De Valera then began to do everything he had said was quite impossible when Michael Collins had proposed it. He decided to use the Treaty to achieve the Republic, and within a short space of time, had got back the Treaty Ports, which were used as British naval bases. He abolished the Governor General and drew up a new Constitution in 1937 and had achieved a total self-govern-ing dominion status, to the extent that the country was neutral in the Second World War. A few years after the war, there was the formal declaration of the Republic by Dáil Éireann.

All the sacrifice, all the blood, all the suffering of the Civil War, had been totally without purpose. The same result could have been achieved in a hand-ful of years by all the talents of the enormous organisation of the IRB working together in friendship, without the cost of a single human life. The greatest loss was in the throwing away of Collins' major achievement in the National position, the Boundary Commission upon which he had pinned his hopes of ending Partition in its infancy.

John Charteris

The death of Collins was a tremendous blow to John Charteris, who was soon working in an obscure civil service job, in an Irish trade mission in Berlin. It was impossible for him to live in England, but he knew that he had powerful enemies in the Free State Government and in the administration, despite the sacrifices he had made and his efforts on behalf of the Republican movement.

At the end of 1922, he was summarily dismissed from his job in Berlin for incautious Republican sympathies, and he obtained a precarious living for a few years after that. In 1925, he was found dead in a small flat in Rathmines. There was no inquest and the cause of his death was never known. His cash assets, in his will, amounted to £486, and a deposit fund of £800.

The Great Cover-Up

The final act in the great series of cover-ups took place in 1932, two nights before the Fianna Fáil Government was elected by Dáil Éireann. Desmond Fitzgerald, who was Minister for Information and Propaganda during the Tan War and the Civil War, led a small party of Free State soldiers down to the basement of Leinster House, carrying numerous bundles of files. These were all carefully placed in the furnaces, burned and the ash carefully raked up. One of them was a brass-bound locked box containing the files on Michael Collins, all the files that had been taken from Dublin Castle, the files on "Thorp" Healy and the files relating to the assassination of Sir Henry Wilson and the attack upon the Four Courts. Fitzgerald himself raked the ashes to make certain that not a single page remained in a legible form.

Northern Division Staff Meeting

In 1943, my mother, Mrs Nora MacDowell shared a cell in Armagh prison, for two years with a woman called Catherine (Cassie) O'Hara, who had been engaged to marry Commandant General Joe McKelvey.

The pair discussed the tragic events of the split and the Civil War, and my mother particularly noted the restrained comments of O'Hara regarding Michael Collins "Poor Mick – he did his best but he was out of his depth," was typical of her comment.

She mentioned that Collins had set up an arrangement with Frank Aiken, of the 4th Northern Division, and with McKelvey, to channel guns and ammunition to the Northern Divisions, in the spring of 1922. On one occasion, she was aware that Collins and Liam Cullen drove out from Dundalk in an army lorry to Crossmaglen and handed over 83 rifles and three boxes of ammunition to Aiken and McKelvey on the understanding that the arms would not be used in the South. This was April or May of 1922.

Later, on 2 August, after the capture of the Four Courts, Collins, as CIC of the Free State Army officially presided at a meeting of divisional officers of the Northern Division to discuss the policies of the Free state government, and the best strategy for Northern Republicans following the outbreak of the Civil War. At that meeting, Collins gave an explicit guarantee that the Four Courts prisoners would be treated with honour and expressed the hope that the civil war would be over in two months.

He reminded the Northern officers that he was also a deputy for South Armagh, and had their interests at heart. He was killed just three weeks later, and Rory O' Connor, Dick Barrett, Liam Mellowes and Joe McKelvey, four leading members of the IRB, were taken out and murdered on 8 December.

Letter from O\C; 3rd Northern Division.

To: General Mulcahy

Commander-in-Chief

Dublin

29th September 1922.

Sir,

As I am inclined to believe, the attitude of the present Government towards its followers in the Six Counties, is not that of General Collins, I am writing this memo with a view to ascertaining from you what exactly the position of my Division is now, and is likely to be in the future relative to GHQ: and I would also like to know through you what policy the Government has for its followers in the Divisional area.

When the Treaty was signed in December last we were given to understand by General O'Duffy that although the Six Counties did not benefit as much as the rest of Ireland by it, it was the best that could possibly be got at the time, and it was the intention of the Dail members and members of the GHQ Staff who supported it, to work to try to overcome the Treaty position with regard to Ulster.

During the three months following the signing of the Treaty I am satisfied that GHQ did their best to assist the Army in the Six Counties, and when the Split came in March, I recommended to officers and men to stand with GHQ as I considered by so doing we were giving the people who supported the Treaty a better chance of overcoming the position in the North.

After the outbreak of hostilities between GHQ and the Executive there was a danger that the position in Ulster would be more or less overlooked, and allowed to drift, and in order to have a definition of our position and of the policy of the Government here, I asked for a meeting of the senior officers of the Six County area.

Before that meeting was held I sent you a memo with the events in the Division from the time I took over command, and outlining the position general at the end of July as regards morale and tactics of the enemy; the morale of our troops and the morale of the Catholic population and their attitude towards the IRA.

On August 2nd, the meeting was held and the late Commander-in-Chief presided. At that meeting the situation in the Six Counties was discussed at great length, with a view to improving our organisation and training and deciding on a policy to be adopted by our people in the North which would have the sanction of the Government in Dublin. The late C-I-C outlined the policy we were to adopt – one of non-recognition of the Northern Government, and any action on our part would be purely protective. The late C-I-C, made it clear to us that the Government in Dublin intended to deal with the Ulster situation in a very definite way, and as far as this Division was concerned every officer present felt greatly encouraged to carry on the work when we had a definite policy to pursue and an assurance that the Government here would stand by us.

After the death of the late General Collins it was encouraging for us to see the Government were determined to carry out his policy. I took this to mean his policy regarding Ulster also.

A new situation has now arisen. F. McArdle (Belfast IRA officer) was up a fortnight ago with President Cosgrave regarding the course of action to be adopted by our people in connection with the signing of a declaration of loyalty to HM the King and the Northern Government, which that Government was imposing on certain people and I expect through time will impose on every citizen in the Six County area. McArdle informed me that the President brought the matter before a meeting of the Cabinet and that the decision was that the Government in Dublin had no objection to our people signing this. Owing to the position that has arisen in the rest of Ireland I take it the Government feel that they are not equal to the task of overcoming the Treaty position with regard to Ulster. If it is their position to recognise the Northern Government, it is well they should be acquainted with the present position in Ulster, and have an idea of what the future of Ulster is likely to be as we visualise it.

There is grave internal trouble in the Northern Government. When their terror policy was broken up by our campaign of burning and destruction in Belfast, they turned to a policy of placation towards the Catholic population and this proved fairly successful, (We, of course, were at this time becoming inactive owing to the War in the rest of Ireland) they began to dispense with their "Specials". A desire for peace became popular with the better classes and the Northern Government took up the task of restoring order in good faith.

There were a number of high officers in the Police Force who had been given unlimited powers during the terror campaign, notably D\I Nixon and all his staff. Such people, while they were in power, would always be a menace to peace, and during the past few months have been pressing for promotion or reward and D\I Nixon was asked to resign.

He is at present organising the disbanded "Specials" and has threatened to lead them against the Northern Government on the same lines as the Irregulars in the South. He has also warned Col.Wickham, Inspector-General of the RUC, and the City Commissioner of Belfast, that their lives are no longer safe. Last week, Nixon and Co attempted to shoot up the Catholic districts of Belfast in the hope that the IRA would take the field, and it would become evident to the Northern Government that there was a necessity to strengthen their forces rather than deplete them. I have issued a special Order against retaliation until we see how the official forces of the Northern Ireland Government are going to deal with this trouble. In a particular area last week in Belfast, the Official Specials returned the fire of some of the Nixon gang: this is a great change in Belfast.

Owing to the capture by us of all the files and plans from HQ RUC and the office of General Solly-Flood, Craig's military adviser, the Northern Government has been holding enquiries in all their departments, and the position at the moment is that every official is suspecting the other.

Recognition of the Northern Government, of course, will mean the breaking up of our Division. None of the Divisional, Brigade or Battalion officers could remain in the area except under guarantee from the Northern Government, if such will be arranged, those men would not be safe from unofficial murder gangs. With the departure of these officers it would not be possible to maintain the IRA organisation, which is the only Irish Organisation in the Six Counties at the present time. The breaking up of this Organisation is the first step to making Partition permanent. If it must come, there is very little hope of organising Ulster on Gaelic lines for a long time.

The Government here (Dublin) still has a certain responsibility to its followers in the Six County area and the following points will require their serious consideration:

(a) The question of our prisoners who are not recognising the Northern Government as per the late C-I-C's instructions.
(b) The position of the people who assisted us during the war against England and who are now singled out for harsh treatment by the Northern Government.
(c) The position of our officers and men who have lost their means of living because of their activities against England.
(d) The position of our officers and men from County Antrim and County Down, who are mostly of farming class, and who cannot return to their homes, and those people who are accordingly victimised.
(e) The question of people who have come away from their areas for no reason whatever and on a plea of being refugees have been taken into Government positions in Dublin. This is encouraging emigration.

On these points, it is essential for me to have definite ruling from you and I would be glad if you would let me have this by Tuesday next 3rd prox. Everyone is anxious to know how and where they stand.

Beir Beannacht.
Seamus Woods: O\C 3rd Northern Division.
State Papers Office - Dublin. (S 1801\A)

There is no record in the State Papers Office of an answer to this plea, from Mulcahy or the Free State Government.

APPENDIX A

The Ambush at Béal na Bláth

All positions indicated are approximate.

1. Cart across road.

2. Mine.

3. Crossley tender stopped here.

4. Touring car stopped on bend and occupants moved back towards armoured car.

5. Armoured car.

6. Point at which Collins died.

7. Position of section who arrived from Béal na Bláth.

8. Laneway which could have been used by armoured car for infiltration.

9. Laneway by which two IRA at 10 retreated.

10. Corner from which retreating IRA fired.

11. Two piers of gate from near which IRA were firing on Crossley tender.

12. Laneway by which three IRA men retreated.

13. Free State troops came up laneway to approximately this point.

14. Entrance to laneway.

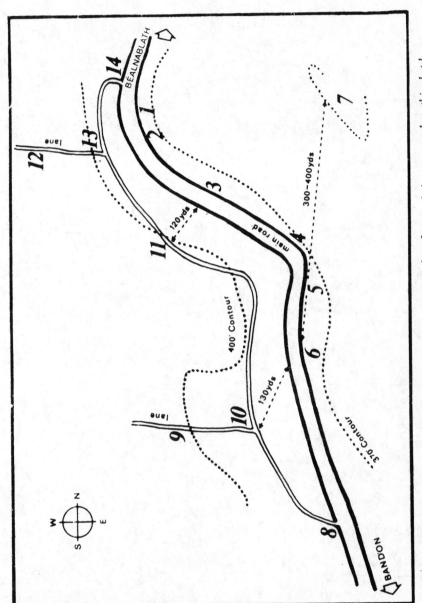

BÉALNABLATH

14

13

12 lane

1

2

11

3

120yds

main road

4

5

6

400° Contour

10

130yds

9 lane

370 Contour

300-400yds

7

8

BANDON

N
W   E
S

Acknowledgment and thanks to the late Captain J.M. Feehan for permission to reproduce this sketch

APPENDIX B

Corry's Account of the Ambush at Béal na Bláth.(2)

"There were two drivers in charge of the car, M. Quinn and myself. Make of car was a Leyland Thomas racing type, straight eight cylinder; no armour of any sort being attached at any time to bodywork or engine; canvas top folded back to rear.

General Collins and Major-General Emmet Dalton were seated in the back, the two drivers in the front seat. We were aware of I.R.A. Flying Column being about at various places during our journey down to Cork; but not a shot was fired at us. We arrived in Cork city at 10.30 p.m. – due to road obstructions, blown bridges, etc.

The day of the ambush

Ahead of us two Crossley tenders with ten armed men in each. Also one Crossley tender containing ropes, saws, picks, food, etc., for emergency use. Leading our column a motor-cyclist guide. At the rear of our car, a Rolls Royce Whippet armoured car, name "Slievenamon".

Two men of the convoy observed the time of departure from Bandon town as being 8 p.m. (G.M.T.) After doing some five miles, we came around a sharp curve and were then on a straight stretch of road. A single shot rang out from across the hill on our extreme left, some 440 yards away (approximately).

General Collins' command "Stop!" was obeyed at once. There was no obstruction on the read ahead of us at the time. On leaving our car, we were met by heavy fire; but no one was hit.

General Collins walked back some fifty yards, followed by Major-General Dalton, Quinn and myself. We took cover at a hedge of ditch about two feet high. The firing was heavy at this time from enemy position right in front. On our extreme right our men were replying. On our extreme left a clear road. At our backs a steep hillside. Firing came from directly in front only.

Major-General Dalton observed that the armoured car machine-gun was not firing. He called to the gunner, who replied, "Gun is jammed, sir".

Gen. Collins, who had been lying firing from a position six feet from me, now stood erect, and after firing several rounds, fell on the roadside, with a gaping wound near the left ear lobe extending to the upper section of the skull; there was also a tear in the front of the forehead, and a hole nipped in the front of his cap close to the badge.

Major–General Dalton said to me, "The General is finished".

We placed the body across the rear seat of the General's car; my hands holding the head, Major–General Dalton the feet of General Collins. Firing had ceased as General Collins died on the roadside. Night fall was coming on and there was some drizzle as we started on our eighteen miles' journey back to Cork."

APPENDIX C

Emmet Dalton's Account of the Ambush at Béal na Bláth

"About three miles from Clonakilty, we found the road blocked with felled trees. We spent about half an hour clearing the road. General Collins, always ready for emergencies, great or small, directed the work, and took a hand in carrying it out. Active and powerful in body as in mind, handled axe and saw with the same vigour as he could exhibit in the direction of affairs of state, military or civil.

Having at last cleared a way, we went into the town of Clonakilty, which is the home town of General Collins. Here he interviewed the garrison officer, and had conversation with many of his friends. It was pleasant to see with what delight and affection they met him. We had lunch in a friend's house in the town before setting out for Roscarbery."

It may be mentioned here that, on his arrival in Clonakilty, the whole town turned out to welcome him.

"Just outside the town of Bandon, General Collins pointed out to me several farmhouses, which he told me were used by the lads in the old days of 'The Terror'. He mentioned to me the home of one particular friend of his own, remarking, 'It's too bad he's on the other side now, because he is a damn good soldier'. Then he added pensively 'I don't suppose I will be ambushed in my own country'.

It was now about a quarter past seven, and the light was failing. We were speeding along the open road on our way to Macroom. Our motor-cyclist scout was about fifty yards in front of the Crossley tender, which we followed at the same interval in the touring car. Close behind us came the armoured car.

We had just reached a part of the road which was commanded by hills on all sides. The road itself was flat and open. On the right we were flanked by steep hills; on the left there was a small two foot bank of earth skirting the road. Beyond this there was a marshy field bounded by a small stream, with another steep hill beyond it.

About half way up this hill there was a road running parallel to the one that we were on, but screened from view by a wall and a mass of trees and bushes. We had just turned a wide corner on the road when a sudden and heavy fusillade of machine-gun and rifle fire swept the road in front of us and behind us, shattering the windscreen of our car.

I shouted to the driver – 'Drive like hell!' But the Commander-in-Chief, placing his hand on the man's shoulder, said – 'Stop! Jump out and we'll fight them.'

We leaped from the car, and took what cover we could behind the little mud bank on the left hand side of the road. It seemed that the greatest volume of fire was coming from the concealed roadway on our left-hand side. The armoured car now backed up the road and opened a heavy machine-gun fire at the hidden ambushers.

It may be mentioned here that the machine-gun in the armoured car 'jammed' after a short time. The machine-gunner, MacPeake not long after this occurrence, deserted to the Irregulars, bringing an armoured car with him.

It was the Crossley tender, which was in charge of Commandant O'Connell which received the first shot. The road had been barricaded by an old cart, which the occupants of the tender promptly removed out of the way. After a few minutes the firing at these ceased, and the ambushers concentrated their fire on Collins and the other men who had occupied the touring car. Sean O'Connell then ran down the road and joined them.

General Collins and I were lying within arm's length of each other. Captain Dolan, who had been on the back of the armoured car, together with our two drivers, was several yards further down the road to my right.

General Collins, and I, with Captain Dolan who was near us, opened a rapid rifle fire on our seldom visible enemies. About fifty or sixty yards further down the road, and round the bend, we could hear that our machine-gunners and riflemen were also heavily engaged.

We continued this fire fight for about twenty minutes without suffering any casualties, when a lull in the enemy's attack became noticeable. General Collins now jumped to his feet and walked over behind the armoured car obviously to obtain a better view of the enemy's position.

He remained there, firing occasional shots and using the car as cover. Suddenly I heard him shout – 'Come on boys! There they are, running up the road.' I immediately opened fire upon two figures that came in view on the opposite road.

When I next turned round the Commander-in-Chief had left the car position, and had run about fifteen yards back up the road. Here he dropped into the prone firing position, and opened up on our retreating enemies.

Dalton, Dolan and O'Connell took up positions on the road further down. Presently the firing of Collins ceased, and Dalton heard, or fancied he heard, a faint cry of "Emmet!" He described how he and Sean O'Connell "rushed to the spot with a dreadful fear clutching our hearts. We found our beloved Chief and friend lying motionless in a firing position, firmly gripping his rifle, across which his head was resting.

There was a fearful gaping wound at the base of the skull behind the right ear. We immediately saw that General Collins was almost beyond human aid. He could not speak to us. The enemy must have seen that something had occurred to cause a sudden cessation of our fire, because they intensified their own.

O'Connell now knelt beside the dying but still conscious Chief, whose eyes were wide open and normal, and he whispered in the ear of the fast-sinking man the words of the Act of Contrition. For this he was rewarded by a slight pressure of the hand.

Meanwhile I knelt beside them both, and kept up bursts of rapid fire, which I continued whilst O'Connell dragged the chief across the road and behind the armoured car. Then, with my heart torn with sorrow and despair, I ran to the Chief's side. Very gently I raised his head on my knee and tried to bandage his wound, but owing to the awful size of it, this proved very difficult.

I had not completed my grievous task when the big eyes closed, and the cold pallor of death overspread the General's face. How can I describe the feelings that were mine at that bleak hour, kneeling in the mud of a country road not twelve miles from Clonakilty, with the still bleeding head of the idol of Ireland resting on my arm.

My heart was broken, my mind was numbed. I was all unconscious of the bullets that still whistled and ripped the ground beside me. I think that the weight of the blow must have caused the loss of my reason had I not abruptly observed the tear-stained face of O'Connell, now distorted with anguish, and calling also for my sympathy and support.

We paused for a moment in silent prayer, and then, noting that the fire of our enemies had greatly abated, and that they had practically all retreated, we two, with the assistance of Lieutenant Smith, the motor-cyclist scout officer, who had come on the scene, endeavoured to lift the stalwart body of Michael Collins on to the back of the armoured car.

It was then that we suffered our second casualty – Lieutenant Smith was shot in the neck. He remained on his feet, however, and helped us to carry our precious burden around a turn in the road and under cover of the armoured car.

Having transferred the body of our Chief to the touring car, where I sat with his head resting on my shoulder, our awe-stricken little party set out for Cork".

APPENDIX D

Mr Barton's Notes

of
Two Sub-Conferences held
on December 5th/6th, 1921, at
10 Downing Street.
No. I ... 3 p.m.
No. II 11.30 p.m. to 2 a.m.

Present:

British Representatives:	*Irish Representatives*
Mr Lloyd George	Mr Griffith
Mr Chamberlain	Mr Collins
Lord Birkenhead	Mr Barton
Mr Churchill	

SUB-CONFERENCE NO. I

3 p.m.

The Conference opened by Lloyd George saying that he must know for once and for all exactly where we stood as regards the Ulster proposals. He said that the Ulster proposals in the document now before us were exactly those to which Arthur Griffith had agreed and on which he had undertaken not to let him (Lloyd George) down.

Arthur Griffith replied that he had not let him down and did not intend to do so, but that before he gave a decision on the earlier articles in the document he must have a reply from Craig either accepting or refusing the unity of Ireland.

Chamberlain and Lloyd George argued that such a proposition was inadmissible, unreasonable and contrary to the undertaking not to let Lloyd George down.

Mr Chamberlain stated that it was due to the confidence they had in our undertaking that they would not be let down by us that his colleagues and he had adopted the attitude they did at the Liverpool meeting and staked thereon their political future.

Michael Collins said that for us to agree to any conditions defining the future relations of Great Britain and Ireland prior to Craig's giving his assent to the unity of Ireland was impossible, that to do so would be to surrender our whole fighting position. That every document we ever sent them had stated that any proposals for the association of Ireland with the British Commonwealth of Nations was conditional upon the unity of Ireland. That, unless

Craig accepted inclusion under the All-Ireland Parliament the unity of Ireland was not assured and that if he refused inclusion we should be left in the position of having surrendered our position without having even secured the essential unity of Ireland.

Lloyd George got excited. He shook his papers in the air, declared that we were trying deliberately to bring about a break on Ulster because our people in Ireland had refused to come within the Empire and that Arthur Griffith was letting him down where he had promised not to do so. He produced a paper from an envelope, stated that he had shewn it to Arthur Griffith at ____'s house and and that Arthur Griffith had agreed to its contents. Lloyd George referred to this document as a letter and thereby mystified me and appeared to mystify Michael Collins. I could not recollect the existence of any letter on this subject other than the one Arthur Griffith wrote to Lloyd George on November 2nd after consultation with the other members of the Delegation. The paper was then passed across the table. It proved to be a memorandum, not a letter, read as follows:

> 'If Ulster did not see her way to accept immediately the principle of a Parliament of All-Ireland – coupled with the retention by the Parliament of Northern Ireland of the powers conferred upon it by the Act of 1920 and such other safeguards as have already been suggested in my letter of 10th November – we should then propose to create such Parliament for All-Ireland but to allow Ulster the right within a specified time on an address to the Throne carried in both houses of the Ulster Parliament to elect to remain subject, to the Imperial Parliament for all the reserved services. In this case she would continue, to exercise through her own Parliament all her present rights; she would continue to be represented in the British Parliament and she would continue subject to British taxation except in so far as already modified by the Act of 1920. In this case, however, it would be necessary to revise the boundary of Northern Ireland. this might be done by a Boundary Commission which would be directed to adjust the line both by inclusion and exclusion so as to make the Boundary conform as closely as possible to the wishes of the population.'

Arthur Griffith declared his adhesion to his undertaking but argued that it was not unreasonable for us to require that Craig should reply before we refused or accepted the proposals now before us.

Lloyd George declared his adhesion to his undertaking but argued that it was not unreasonable for us to require, that Craig should reply before we refused or accepted the proposals now before us.

Lloyd George declared that to make receipt of such a reply conditional before accepting or refusing was letting him down on his proposals because the only alternative to Craig's acceptance of the unity of Ireland was the Boundary Commission and that his Government would carry the Boundary Commission proposal into effect with strict fidelity. He then said that they would have to withdraw to discuss the matter amongst themselves but first he would hear what objections or alterations we had to the proposal.

Arthur Griffith replied that he understood from Michael Collins' interview with Lloyd George that certain alterations might possibly be made in the proposals.

Lloyd George asked what were the alterations we suggested but that we must understand [*sic*] that the first three Clauses were absolutely essential. There could be no discussion about these.

Arthur Griffith replied that some alteration might be made in the Oath.

Birkenhead said that Mr. Collins had handed in to him that morning a form of oath on which he (Mr. Collins) had been working and then produced it with his (Birkenhead's) alterations. We objected to the final words being 'British Empire' and suggested 'British Commonwealth of Nations'.

Lloyd George asked for any further objections.

We objected to 'shall contribute in Clause 5, and desired insertion of 'if any' after 'such sums' and elsewhere.

Chamberlain said that these alterations were matters of wording only. On Clause 6 we argued at great length that the word 'exclusively' precluded us from commencing to build vessels or making any preparation for taking over our own coastal defence at any time and that the 'Conference for Review' referred to in the second paragraph might never be held if the British did not wish to reconsider the subject. There was a long argument over this in which Churchill, Michael Collins and myself went over all the arguments again.

Churchill stated that if Ireland were permitted any navy it would be impossible to get the Treaty through Parliament. That the English people would believe that we were going to build ships which in war might be used against them. That the possibility of our building submarines or mine-laying vessels to attack their food ships would be argued from every angle. The discussion lasted a long time. We demanded the removal of the word 'exclusively'; this was grudgingly accorded. We then sought to get it explicitly stated that Ireland should be required to build one or more ships for her coastal protection; this was absolutely refused, except as regards revenue and fishery protection ships, and Churchill stated definitely oppose any provision that Ireland should have a navy of her own and would even oppose it five years hence if he had the opportunity.

Michael Collins then took up the Trade Clause and said that Lloyd George had intimated that freedom on both sides might be accorded. He also dealt with the suggestion that the safeguards for Ulster should be a rather for discussion between ourselves and the Ulster representatives.

The British then withdrew and we consulted amongst ourselves and decided that if they came back to break on our refusal to accept or refuse pending Craig's answer that Arthur Griffith's last card was so demand reference to the Colonial Premiers.

Birkenhead then returned alone and took note again of the particular points we required changed.

On their return we again took up the points in dispute. First in Clause 6, to which Churchill agreed to add 'with a view to the undertaking by Ireland of a share of her own coastal defence', and to a date years hence being fixed for the Conference to review the Clause, but refused every proposition to make this apply to (b) facilities in time of war.' He refused to take 'Queenstown' out of the Annex, and explained that care and maintenance parties meant gunners and trained men to take charge drawn from the R.G.A. and R.E., numbering 1,060 men and 69 officers or thereabouts. He also stated that 'Admiralty property and rights' at Berehaven did not mean that, they would demand compensation if at any time the docks etc. passed to us. Birkenhead said that if they were handed over to the Crown representative in Ireland the Crown could not demand payment from the Crown.

Lloyd George said that on Trade he was prepared to agree provisionally that there should be freedom on both sides to impose any tariffs either liked subject to the Articles of Agreement being accepted by us. That he himself had been the strongest on their side on the compulsory Free State Clauses, but that he would withdraw his opposition on the conditions stated.

We then went back to Ulster.

Arthur Griffith agreed that he personally would sign the Treaty whether Craig accepted or not, but that his colleagues were in a different position from himself in that they were not party to the promise not to let Lloyd George down, and that it was not fair to demand acceptance or refusal from them before Craig replied.

Considerable discussion took place here on the justice and injustice of our being asked to agree or disagree before Craig replied and Arthur Griffith made repeated efforts to avoid the question being put to Michael Collins and myself.

Lloyd George stated that he had always taken it that Arthur Griffith spoke for the Delegation, that we were all plenipotentiaries and that it was now a matter of peace or war and we must each of us make up our minds. He required that every delegate should sign the document and recommend it, or there was no agreement. He said that they as a body had hazarded their political future and we must do likewise and take the same risks. At one time he particularly addressed himself to me and said very solemnly that those who were not for peace must take the full responsibility for the war that would immediately follow refusal by any Delegate to sign the Articles of Agreement.

He then produced two letters one of which he said he must that night sent (*sic*) to Craig. One was a covering letter to H.M. Government's proposals for the future relations of Ireland and Great Britain and stated that the Irish Delegation had agreed to recommend them for acceptance by Dáil Éireann. The other stated that the Irish Delegation had failed to come to an agreement with H.M. Government and therefore he had no proposals to send to Craig.

Lloyd George stated that he would have to have our agreement or refusal to the proposals by 10 p.m. that evening. That a special train and destroyer were ready to carry either one letter or the other to Belfast and that he would give us until ten o'clock to decide.

We then argued that the twelve months' transition period was of the greatest danger to our people. Craig could say 'yes' at any time, he could say 'No' finally before six months but he need not know whether there was to be unity or not. Meantime life might be made intolerable for our people in Ulster.

Lloyd George argued that that contingency had been apparent from the first, but if it were a serious stumbling block we could shorten the transition period at any time we chose.

Michael Collins said that the recent occurrences in Tyrone-the seizure of the County Council books, etc., and the support of the Ulster Government with English troops had shaken our confidence in their fidelity.

Lloyd George answered that they had no jurisdiction on this matter in Ulster. It was a matter over which the Northern Government had complete control under the 1920 Act. He then suggested that they should withdraw in order that we might discuss the duration of the transition period amongst ourselves. They did so.

We decided to reduce the period to one month. Rang for them to return and stated our decision.

Lloyd George said he considered the decision ill advised as a month did not give the Ulster people sufficient time to reflect. He affirmed that Craig was going to refuse the terms and that he (Lloyd George) knew this for certain. However, as we preferred one month he was prepared to accept the alteration and redraft the Clauses. A month was the least possible that could be given Craig to make a final decision. He then proposed that we dismiss and reassemble again at 10 to give him our final decision.

There was a discussion amongst ourselves lasting from 9 to 11.15 at 22 Hans Place, at which a decision was eventually reached to recommend the Treaty to the Dáil.

SUB-CONFERENCE NO. II

11.15 p.m.-2.20 a.m.

At 11.30 we returned to Downing Street and attacked the document again. We endeavoured to get Clause 3 removed, but failed. We, however, succeeded in getting the word 'Governor-General' out, it being left to decide upon a term. The title 'President', Chamberlain stated, was inadmissible.

Michael Collins demanded and secured the removal of the word 'local' as a prefix to the Irish Free State's military defence force.

They agreed to the verbal changes in financial Clause 5. Chamberlain took exception to the 'if anys' going in, as he said it. too late to quibble over such small points. We pointed out that Clause 9 was still left intact and that it should have been removed under the agreement on 8. Lloyd George said that it referred to transport only. It meant ships entering harbours and that there must be provision to prevent boycotting of English shipping. Birkenhead said that the wording of the clause was ambiguous now that the compulsory Free Trade clause was gone and suggested redrafting it. This was done immediately.

Michael Collins queried the reference to summoning of the Southern-Ireland Parliament in Clauses 15 and 17, and Birkenhead immediately drafted an explanatory memorandum as follows:

'It is intended by Clauses 15 and 17 to make it plain that the functions therein referred to shall be discharged by the Provisional Government of Southern Ireland and that for that purpose a transfer shall be made by them of the necessary powers under the Government of Ireland Act, 1920, as soon as the mutual notifications have been exchanged.

The Provisional Government will it is contemplated upon such ratification undertake the Govert. of S. Ireland immediately until the necessary Acts in both Parliaments confer upon it the statutory authority contemplated in this instrument.

B.'

Lloyd George then asked whether we as a Delegation were prepared to accept these Articles of Agreement and to stand by them in our Parliament as they as a Delegation would stand by them in theirs.

Arthur Griffith replied, 'We do.'

We then discussed the release of the prisoners and procedure for ratification and other matters whilst awaiting the final draft.

The final draft was read over, agreed to and signed; also the Annex.

THE BRITISH DELEGATION lined up to shake hands and say goodbye, and the Conference ended at 2.20 a.m. on December 6th.

Robert Barton

APPENDIX E

Political Thinking: Buiding up Ireland

Resources to be Developed

Mr. De Valera, in a speech he made on February 19, warned the people of Ireland against a life of ease, against living practically 'the life of the beasts', which, he fears, they may be tempted to do in Ireland under the Free State.

The chance that materialism will take possession of the Irish people is no more likely in a free Ireland under the Free State than it would be in a free Ireland under a Republican or any other form of government. It is in the hands of the Irish people themselves.

In the ancient days of Gaelic civilization the people were prosperous and they were not materialists. They were one of the most spiritual and one of the most intellectual peoples in Europe. When Ireland was swept by destitution and, famine the spirit of the Irish people came most nearly to extinction. It was with the improved economic conditions of the last twenty years or more that it has re-awakened. The insistent needs of the body more adequately satisfied, the people regained desire once more to reach out to the higher things in which the spirit finds its satisfaction.

What we hope for in the new Ireland is to have such material welfare as will give the Irish spirit that freedom. We want such widely diffused prosperity that the Irish people will not be crushed by destitution into living practically 'the lives of the beasts'.

They were so crushed during the British occupation that they where described as being 'without the comforts of an English sow'. Neither must they be obliged, owing to unsound economic conditions, to spend all their powers of both mind and body in an effort to satisfy the bodily needs alone. The uses of wealth are to provide good health, comfort, moderate luxury, and to give the freedom which comes from the possession of these things.

Our object in building up the country economically must not be lost sight of. That object is not to be able to boost of enormous wealth or of a great volume of trade, for their own sake. It is not to see our country covered with smoking chimneys and factories. It is not to show a great national balance-sheet, not to point to a people producing wealth with the self-obliteration of a hive of bees.

The real riches of the Irish nation will be the men and women of the Irish nation, the extent to which they are rich in body and mind and character.

What we want is the opportunity for everyone to be able to produce sufficient wealth to ensure these advantages for themselves. That such wealth can be produced in Ireland there can be no doubt:

> 'For the island is so endowed with so many dowries of nature, considering the fruitfulness of the soil, the ports, the rivers, the fishing, and especially the race and generation of men; valiant, hard, and active, as it is not easy to find such a confluence of commodities.'

Such was the impression made upon a visitor who came long ago to our island. We have now the opportunities to make our land indeed fruitful, to work up our natural resources, to bring prosperity for all our people.

If our national economy is put on a sound footing from the beginning it will, in the new Ireland, be possible for our people to provide themselves with the ordinary requirements of decent living. It will be possible for each to have sufficient food, a good home in which to live in fair comfort and contentment. We shall be able to give our children bodily and mental health; and our people will be able to secure themselves against the inevitable times of sickness and old age.

What must be our object. *What we must aim at is the building up of a sound economic life in which great discrepancies cannot occur.* We must not have the destitution of poverty at one end, and at the other an excess of riches in the possession of a few individuals, beyond what they can spend with satisfaction and justification.

Millionaires can spend their surplus wealth bestowing libraries broadcast upon the world. But who will say that the benefits accruing could compare with those arising from a condition of things in which the people themselves everywhere, in the city, town, and village, were prosperous enough to buy their own books and to put together their own local libraries in which they could take a personal interest and acquire knowledge in proportion to that interest?

The growing wealth of Ireland will, we hope, be diffused through all our people, all sharing in the growing prosperity, each receiving according to what each contributes in the making of that prosperity, so that the weal of all is assured.

How are we to increase, the wealth of Ireland and ensure that all producing it shall share in it? That is the question which will be engaging the minds of our people, and will engage the attention of the new Government.

The keynote to the economic revival must be development of Irish resources by Irish capital for the benefit of the Irish consumer in such a way that the people have steady work at just remuneration and their own share of control.

How are we to develop Irish resources? The earth is our bountiful mother. Upon free access to it depends not only agriculture, but all other trades and industries. Land must be freely available. Agriculture, our main industry, must be improved and developed. Our existing industries must be given opportunities to expand. Conditions must be created which will make it possible for, new ones to arise. Means of transit must be extended and cheapened. Our harbours must be developed. Our water-power must be utilised; our mineral resources must be exploited.

Foreign trade must be stimulated by making facilities for the transport and marketing of Irish goods abroad and foreign goods in Ireland. Investors must be urged and encouraged to invest Irish capital in Irish concerns. Taxation, where it hinders, must be adjusted, and must be imposed where the burden will fall lightest and can best be borne, and where it will encourage rather than discourage industry.

We have now in Ireland, owing to the restrictions put upon emigration during the European War; a larger population of young men and women than we have had for a great many years. For their own sake and to maintain the strength of the nation room must and can be found for them.

Agriculture is, and is likely to continue to be, our chief source of wealth. If room is to be found for our growing population, land must be freely available. Land is not freely available in Ireland. Thousands of acres of the best land lie idle or are occupied as ranches or form part of extensive private estates.

Side by side with this condition there are thousands of our people who are unable to get land on which to keep a cow or even to provide themselves and their families with vegetables.

If the ranches can be broken up, if we can get the land back again into the hands of our people, there will be plenty of employment and a great increase in the national wealth.

If land could be obtained more cheaply in town and county the housing problem would not present so acute a problem. There are large areas unoccupied in towns and cities as well as in country districts. When the Convention sat in 1917 it was found that in urban areas alone 67,000 houses were urgently needed. The figure must at the present moment be considerably higher. To ease the immediate situation, the Provisional Government has announced a grant to enable a considerable number of houses to be built. This grant, although seemingly large, is simply a recognition of the existence of the problem.

For those who intend to engage in agriculture we require specialised education. Agriculture is in these days a highly technical industry. We have the experience of countries like Holland, Germany, Denmark to guide us. Scientific methods of farming and stock-raising must be introduced. We must have the study of specialised chemistry to aid us, as it does our foreign competitors in the countries I have named. *We must establish industries arising directly out of agriculture*, industries for the utilisation of the by products of the land-bones, bristles, hides for the production of soda glue, and other valuable substances.

With plenty of land available at an economic rent or price such industries can be established throughout the country districts, opening up new opportunities for employment.

Up to the sixteenth century Ireland possessed a colonial trade equal to England's. It was destroyed by the jealousy of English ship owners and manufacturers, and, by means of the Navigation Law England swept Ireland's commerce off the seas. It is true that these Navigation Laws were afterwards removed. But the removal found the Irish capital which might have restored our ruined commerce drained away from the country by the absence of opportunities for utilising it, or by absentee landlordism, or in other ways.

The development of industry in the new Ireland should be on lines which exclude monopoly profits. The product of industry would thus be left sufficiently free to supply good wages to those employed in it. *The system should be on co-operative lines rather than on the old commercial capitalistic lines of the huge joint stock companies.* At the same time I think we shall safely avoid State Socialism, which has nothing to commend it in a country like Ireland, and, in any case, is monopoly of another kind.

Given favourable conditions, there is a successful future for dressed meat industries on the lines of the huge co-operative industry started in Wexford; while there are many opportunities for the extension of dairying and cheese-making.

The industries we possess are nearly all capable of expansion.

We can improve and extend all the following:

Brewing and distilling.

Manufacture of tobacco.

Woollen and linen industry.

Manufacture of hosiery and underclothing.

Rope and twine industry.

Manufacture of boots and shoes, saddlery, and all kinds of leather articles.

Production of hardware and agricultural machinery.

Production and curing of fish.

Of manufactured articles £48,000,000 worth are imported into Ireland yearly. A large part of these could be produced more economically at home. If land were procurable abundantly and cheaply it would be necessary also that capital should be forth coming to get suitable sites for factories, a more easily obtained supply of power, and improvement, increase, and cheapening of the means of transport.

There are facilities for producing and enormous variety of products both for the home and foreign markets, if factories could be established. These should, as far as possible, be dispersed about the country instead of being concentrated in a few areas. This will incidentally improve the status and earnings of the country population and will enlarge their horizon.

I am not advocating the establishment of an industrial system as other countries know industrialism. If we are to survive as a distinct and free nation, industrial development must be on the general lines I am following. Whatever our solution of the question may be, we all realise that the industrial *status quo* is imperfect. However we may differ in outlook, politically or socially, it is recognised that one of the most pressing needs – if not the most pressing – is the question of labour in relation to industry, and it is consequently vitally necessary for the development of our resources that the position of employers and employees should rest on the best possible foundation.

And with this question of labour and industry is interwoven the question of land. It is no less important to have our foundations secure here. In the development of Ireland the land question presents itself under four main headings:

(1) The completion of purchase of tenants land;

(2) The extension and increase of powers of purchase of untenanted lands;

(3) the question of congestion in rural districts;

(4) the utilisation of land unoccupied or withheld in urban areas

For the purpose of such development Ireland has three great natural resources. Our coal deposits are by no means inconsiderable. The bogs of Ireland are estimated as having 500,000 million tons of peat fuel. Water-power is concentrated in her 237 rivers and 180 lakes. *The huge Lough Corrib system could be utilised, for instance, to work the granite in the neighbourhood of Galway.* In the opinion of experts, reporting to the Committee on the Water–Power Resources of Ireland, from the Irish lakes and rivers a total of 500,000 h.p. is capable of being developed.

The magnitude of this is more readily seen if it is appreciated that to raise this power in steam would require 7,500,000 tons of coal. With the present price of coal it should be a commercial proposition to develop our water-power as against steam, even through it did not take the place of steam-power entirely.

Schemes have been worked out to utilise the water-power of the Shannon, the Erne, the Bann, and the Liffey. It is probable that the Liffey and the Bann, being closely connected with industrial centres, can be dealt with at once. With unified control and directions, various sources of water-power could be arranged in large stations for centralised industries, and the energy could be re-distributed to provide light and heat for the neighbouring towns and villages.

That the advantages of our water-power are not lost on some of the keenest minds of the day is shown by the following extract from a speech made by Lord Northcliffe on St. Patrick's Day, 1917. 'The growth of the population of Great Britain has been largely due to manufactures based on the great asset, black coal. Ireland had none of that coal which has made England rich, but she possesses in her mighty rivers white coal of which millions of horse-power are being lost to Ireland every year. . . . I can see in the future very plainly prosperous cities, old and new, fed by the greatest river in the United Kingdom _ the

Shannon. I should like to read recent experts' reports on the Moy, the Suir, and the Lee.'

The development of this white power will also enable the means of communication and transport by rail and road to be cheapened and extended. And there is an urgent need for cheap transit. Railway rates and shipping rates are so high that, to take one example, the cost of transit is prohibitive to the Irish fish trade.

While the Irish seas are teeming with fish, we have the Dublin market depending upon the English market for its supplies. The export of Irish fish is decreasing, and the fishing industry is neither the source of remuneration it should be to those engaged in it, nor the source of profit it could be to the country.

To facilitate the transport of agricultural produce and commodities generally, a complete system of ways of communication must be established. *The extension and unifying of our railways*, linking up ocean ports and fishing harbours with the interior, is essential. This system will be worked in connection with our inland waterways, an will be supplemented by a motor-lorry service on our roads – and these also must be greatly improved.

Our harbours must be developed. Ireland occupies a unique geographical position. She is the stepping-stone between the Old World and the New. She should, therefore, become a great exchange mart between Europe and America. With Galway harbour improved and developed so as to receive American liners, passengers could land in Europe one or two days earlier than by disembarking at Liverpool.

The port and docks of Dublin are already making arrangements for a great increase in the volume of trade which is expected with the establishment of an Irish Government in Dublin. They are improving the port. They have schemes for providing deep water berthage for the largest ships afloat.

Soon the port of Dublin will be fitted in every way to receive and deal with all the trade which may be expected with our growing prosperity. The Board is also reclaiming land at the mouth of the Liffey, and soon some sixty acres will be available as a building site. This land is splendidly situated for commercial purposes.

It will be important to create efficient machinery for the economic marketing of Irish goods. A first step in this direction is the establishment of a clearing house in Dublin or the most convenient centre. It would form a link between a network of channels throughout Ireland through which goods could be transmitted, connecting with another network reaching out to all our markets abroad. It would examine and take delivery of goods going out and coming in, dealing with the financial business for both sides.

Such a concern would require capital and able and experienced management. With such, its success should be assured. It would be invaluable in helping our home and foreign trade. And with improved means of transit in Ireland, and an increase in the number of direct shipping routes, facilities would be in existence to make it operate successfully. It is not difficult to see the advantages of such a house. *On the one hand it would be closely associated in location and business working with a central railway station where the important trunk lines converged and on the other conveniently situated to the National Customs House.*

The mineral resources of Ireland have never been properly tapped. An Irish Government will not neglect this important source of wealth. The development of mines and minerals will be on national mines, and under national direction. *This will prevent the monopoly by private individuals of what are purely national resources belonging to all the people of the nation. The profits from all these national enterprises-the working of mines, development of water-power, etc. – will belong to the nation for the advantage of the whole nation.*

But Irish men and women as private individuals must do their share to increase the prosperity of the country. Business cannot succeed without capital. Millions of Irish money are lying idle in banks. The deposits in Irish joint stock banks increased in the aggregate by £7,318,000 during the half-year ended December 31, 1921. At that date the total of deposits and cash balances in the Irish banks was £194,391,000, to which in addition there was a sum of almost £14,000,000 in the Post Office Savings Bank. If Irish money were invested in Irish industries, to assist existing ones, and to finance new enterprises, there would be an enormous development of Irish commerce.

The Irish people have a large amount of capital invested abroad. With scope for our energies, with restoration of confidence, the inevitable tendency will be towards return of this capital to Ireland. It will then flow in its proper channel. It will be used for opening up new and promising fields in this country. Ireland will provide splendid opportunities for the investment of Irish capital, and it is for the Irish people to take advantage of these opportunities.

If they do not, investors and exploiters from outside will come in to reap the rich profits which are to be made. And, what is worse still, they will bring with them all the evils that we want to avoid in the new Ireland.

We shall hope to see in Ireland industrial conciliation and arbitration taking the place of strikes, and the workers sharing in the ownership and management of businesses.

A prosperous Ireland will mean a united Ireland. With equitable taxation and flourishing trade our North-East countrymen will need no persuasion to come and share in the healthy economic life of the country.

Michael Collins

APPENDIX F

Anglo-Irish Treaty ... The Boundary Commission

Article 12:

If before the expiration of the said month, an address is presented to His Majesty by both Houses of Parliament of Northern Ireland to that effect the powers of the Parliament and Government of the Irish Free State shall no longer extend to Northern Ireland, and the provisions of the Government of Ireland Act, 1920 (including those relating to the Council of Ireland) shall, so far as they relate to Northern Ireland, continue to be of full force and effect, and this instrument shall have effect subject to the necessary modifications.

Provided that if such an address is so presented a Commission consisting of three persons, one to be appointed by the Government of the Irish Free State and one to be appointed by the Government of Northern Ireland and one who shall be Chairman to be appointed by the British Government shall determine in accordance with the wishes of the inhabitants, so far as may be compatible with economic and geographic conditions, the boundaries between Northern Ireland and the rest of Ireland, and for the purposes of the Government of Ireland Act, 1920, and of this instrument, the boundary of Northern Ireland shall be such as may be determined by such Commission.

Index

Maguire, Tom, 86
Malone, Tom 141, 142
Mansion House 51, 52, 54
Markham, Thomas 72
Markievitz, Countess Constance 12, 27, 52
Marquis of Londonderry 15
Martyn, Hazel 20
Martyn, Mrs Edward 20, 21
Mason, Sinead 62
Maxwell, General 39
McArdle, F. 162
McCabe, Alex 37
McCartan, Doctor Pat 48
McCarthaigh, Conor 129
McCarthy, Justin 12
McClean, Captain 21
McCormack, Michael 86
McCrea, Pat 55
McCready, General 71, 97, 125, 127
McCullough, Dennis 34, 37
McCurtain, Tomas 67
McDermot, Sean 32
McDonald, Ramsey 100
McDonnell, Andy 87
McDonnell, Mike 55
McGarry, Joe 42
McGrath Joe 119, 129, 151, 155
McGuinness, J.J. 43, 133
McGuinness, Joseph 122
McKee, Richard 76, 77, 78
McKenna, Bill 139, 140, 141
McKenna, Kathleen 70
McMahon, John 34, 154
McMahon, Sir James 48
McMahon Family 124
McNamara 55
McNeill, Eoin 16, 29, 35, 92, 123, 129, 135, 151
Mellows, Liam 12, 32, 83, 122, 128, 132, 151, 161
MI5 71, 72
MI6 71, 101, 134, 135, 141, 149, 150
Moore Street 27
Mountjoy Prison 70, 126, 152
Moylan, Sean 122, 132
Moyvore 32
Mulcahy, Richard 32, 35, 36, 53, 76,

77, 81, 83, 85, 106, 107, 117, 119, 121, 127, 129, 130, 146, 147, 148, 150, 152, 154, 158
Mullins, Bill 34

National Army 116,153
Neligan, David 55, 102, 139, 140
Nixon, D/I 163

O'Brien, Conor Cruise 17
O'Cannain, Seamus 141
O'Connell, Commandant 29
O'Connell, General Ginger 127, 145
O'Connor, James 10, 20
O'Connor, Moya 10, 18
O'Connor, Rory 99, 120, 123, 125, 127, 128, 151, 161
O'Donnell, Pat 72
O'Donoghue, Florence 50, 81, 82, 83, 134, 136, 142
O'Donovan Rossa, Jeremiah 7, 10, 45, 146
O'Duffy, General Eoin 107, 130, 152, 154, 161
O'Dywer, Seamus 122, 132
O'Hagerty, Sean 122
O'Hanrahan, Michael 32
O'Hara, Catherine 160
O'Hegarty, Diarmuid 34, 41, 53, 103
O'Higgins, Kevin 59,73, 74, 98, 116, 122, 123, 128, 129, 130, 131, 132, 134, 135, 137, 147, 148, 150, 151, 152, 154, 155
O'Kelly, Sean T. 48, 49, 51, 104, 157, 159
O'Leary, John 10
O'Mahony, John 7
O'Maille, Padraig 35, 122, 149
O'Malley, Earnan 86, 91, 120, 128
O'Muirthuile, Liam 42, 107, 155
O'Muirthuile, Sean 34, 117, 156
O'Neill, Colonel John 9
O'Rahilly, The 29
O'Reilly, Joe 35, 55, 139, 140
O'Reilly, M.W. 37
O'Shaughnessy, Garrett 7
O'Sullivan 124, 134
Oath of Loyalty 86